NONAQUEOUS SOLVENTS

RALPH A. ZINGARO

PROFESSOR OF CHEMISTRY
TEXAS A&M UNIVERSITY

D. C. HEATH AND COMPANY
A division of RAYTHEON EDUCATION COMPANY
LEXINGTON, MASSACHUSETTS

LIBRARY OF CONGRESS CATALOG CARD NUMBER 68-12481

Preface

The purpose of this book is to introduce the reader to the subject of nonaqueous solvents in a manner which is more detailed and technical than that usually encountered in the general coverage in undergraduate courses in inorganic chemistry. The limitations imposed by space requirements of this book have restricted both the number of solvents which can be discussed and the degree of detail which can be included for those which are discussed.

A basic solvent, liquid ammonia; an acidic solvent, hydrogen fluoride; and an aprotic solvent, sulfur dioxide, have been covered. Because several recent texts and reviews, which are referred to in the bibliography, discuss these and the other more widely studied solvents in much greater detail, the discussion of these solvents in this book is not as detailed as the material on liquid-liquid extraction and fused salt systems. The latter are topics ordinarily not included in discussions of nonaqueous solvents. For this reason they receive more extensive coverage here; some original experimental work has been presented in detail.

The author has very often been confronted with the question "What good is all this?", For this reason examples of the practical applications of research in nonaqueous solvents have been included.

In presenting the material on liquid-liquid extraction and fused salt systems I have drawn considerable information from my own work and that of my colleagues. This I have done only because greater familiarity with the material has enabled me to present it clearly yet concisely. There has been no intention to slight the efforts of numerous, highly competent investigators to whom proper recognition cannot be given in a limited coverage of this kind.

The exercises at end of chapters are not of the "drill" type. Rather, they are intended to supplement the coverage and to extend the study to topics which should have been, but could not be, included. The exercises are suitable as subjects for written and oral reports.

Ralph A. Zingaro

Acknowledgments

Figures 3–1, 3–2, 6–3, 6–4, 6–5, 6–6, 6–7, 7–1, 7–2, 7–4, 7–7, 7–8, 7–9 and Table 7–2 were reproduced with permission from the American Chemical Society. Table 3–3 was reproduced with permission from the Academic Press; figures 4–1 and 7–3 by consent of the Electrochemical Society, Inc., and figures 5–1, 6–1, 6–2, and 7–6 with the permission of John Wiley and Sons, Inc. I wish to thank these organizations for allowing the use of this material.

Contents

Chapter 1 *Introduction*

1–A General Remarks.. 1
1–B Water—Its Limitations as a Solvent........................... 2
1–C Classification of Solvents...................................... 4
Exercises... 7
References.. 8

Chapter 2 *Acids and Bases and Some Theories Dealing with the Behavior of Solutes in Nonaqueous Solvents*

2–A The Arrhenius Theory of Acids and Bases....................... 9
2–B The Brönsted-Lowry Theory of Acids and Bases.................. 10
2–C The Theory of Solvent Systems or Ionotropy.................... 12
2–D The Lewis Concept... 14
2–E The Usanovich Theory.. 16
2–F The Coordination Model for the Behavior of Solutes in Nonaqueous Solvents.. 16
Exercises... 19
References.. 19

Chapter 3 *Liquid Ammonia as a Solvent*

3–A Some Problems Which Must Be Solved When Working with Nonaqueous Solvents... 20
3–B Ammonia and Hydrogen Fluoride as Solvents—General Considerations... 21
3–C Solubility of Metals in Liquid Ammonia........................ 22
3–D Some Reactions in Liquid Ammonia............................. 26
3–E The Utility of Studies in Liquid Ammonia...................... 30
3–F Hydrocarbons as Acids and Bases.............................. 32
3–G Mechanism of Exchange and Isomerization in Unsaturated Hydrocarbons.. 33
Exercises... 35
References.. 35

Chapter 4 *Anhydrous Hydrogen Fluoride*

4–A General Considerations.. 36
4–B Solvent Properties of Hydrogen Fluoride Toward Inorganic Substances 37
4–C Solubility of Organic Compounds in Hydrogen Fluoride.......... 39
4–D Inorganic Reactions Involving Acid-Base Relationships......... 39
4–E Organic Reactions in Liquid Hydrogen Fluoride................. 41
4–F Electrolysis of Organic Compounds in Anhydrous Hydrogen Fluoride 41
4–G Preparation of the Freons..................................... 43
4–H Addition of Hydrogen Fluoride to Unsaturated Bonds........... 44

Exercises.. 45
References... 45

Chapter 5 *Liquid Sulfur Dioxide and a Little about Phosgene*

5–A General Considerations..................................... 46
5–B Solubility of Inorganic Substances......................... 48
5–C Solubility of Organic Compounds........................... 48
5–D Acid-Base Reactions in Liquid Sulfur Dioxide.............. 49
5–E Metathetical Reactions in Liquid Sulfur Dioxide........... 50
5–F Complex Compound Formation............................... 51
5–G Tracer Studies in Liquid Sulfur Dioxide................... 52
5–H Ionization of Thionyl Halides in Liquid Sulfur Dioxide.... 54
5–I Sulfur Dioxide in the Petroleum Industry.................. 55
5–J Organic Reactions in Liquid Sulfur Dioxide................ 56
5–K The Theory of Solvent Systems and Tracer Experiments in Phosgene 57
Exercises.. 58
References... 58

Chapter 6 *Liquid-Liquid Solvent Extraction*

6–A Some Historical Background................................ 59
6–B General Considerations.................................... 60
6–C Distribution of the Solute in the Form of Neutral Molecules....... 62
6–D Extraction of Halometallic Acids......................... 63
6–E Organophosphorus Compounds as Extractants................ 66
6–F Alkali Metal Ion Separation by Liquid-Liquid Solvent Extraction.... 71
6–G Other Reagents of Importance............................. 77
Exercises.. 77
References... 77

Chapter 7 *Fused Salt Systems*

7–A General Considerations.................................... 79
7–B Some Experimental Techniques Used in Fused Salt Research....... 80
7–C Some Applications of Fused Salt Chemistry................. 85
7–D Acid-Base Theory in Molten Nitrates...................... 86
7–E Spectrophotometric Studies in Molten Fluoride Salts...... 89
7–F Spectra of the Transition Metal Ions of the First Series.... 90
7–G Solutions of Metals with Molten Salts.................... 95
7–H Metals that Dissolve with Subhalide Formation............ 100
7–I Concluding Remarks....................................... 103
Exercises.. 103
References... 104

CHAPTER *1*

Introduction

1–A GENERAL REMARKS

During exposure to the conventional chemistry curriculum it becomes apparent to the student that the vast majority of chemical reactions takes place in solution. It is further obvious that water is the principal solvent in which inorganic reactions occur. It is quite evident that ours is a "water-world."

Perhaps the most striking manifestation of the vital importance of water to the maintenance of life is the gradual reduction in the numbers of living organisms which is observed as one proceeds from an area of adequate water supply to a more arid region. There appears to be an almost complete absence of living matter in the truly arid regions such as the Arabian and Sahara deserts as well as in our own Death Valley. Western civilization was born and developed and flourished in regions close to adequate water supplies. Man needed water, then, as now, for his very sustenance: for the irrigation of his fields, the operation of his industries, and the movement of his products. Bodies of water furnished food and necessary recreation. The Mediterranean Sea served as an avenue of water transportation, and the valleys of the Nile, Tigris, Euphrates, and Tiber rivers were the arterial connections where early civilizations thrived.

So, it is not by any accident but because of the very nature of our physiological and psychological make-up that we have always possessed a long and continuing devotion to water.

1

It is virtually certain that water will never be displaced, at least on this planet, as the most commonly used solvent. While its virtues are obvious, it does have certain limitations.

1–B   WATER—ITS LIMITATIONS AS A SOLVENT

Under ordinary atmospheric pressure, water exists as a liquid in the temperature range from 0–100°C; this means that reactions in this solvent at ordinary pressures are restricted to this range of temperature. In order to better appreciate the solvent properties of water, let us consider the dissolution of magnesium sulfate in this solvent. When *anhydrous* magnesium sulfate is dissolved in water heat is *given off*, and the enthalpy of solution is said to be negative. This reaction may be represented by writing

$$MgSO_4(s) + n\,H_2O$$
$$\rightleftarrows Mg(H_2O)_{n-x}^{+2}(aq) + SO_4(H_2O)_x^{-2}(aq) \qquad -\Delta H_1 \quad (1)$$

The number of water molecules arranged in the nearest layer around the ions, indicated in this example by $(H_2O)_{n-x}$ and $(H_2O)_x$ is known as the *coordination number*, or *hydration number*, of the ion. Because cations are smaller than anions, the forces of attraction between a cation and the negative ends of the water dipoles are considerably stronger than those between the larger anions and the positive ends of the water dipoles.

When *hydrated* magnesium sulfate, $MgSO_4 \cdot 7\,H_2O$, is dissolved in water, the enthalpy of solution is positive, i.e., heat is *absorbed* from the surroundings, and we may write this reaction as

$$MgSO_4 \cdot 7\,H_2O(s) + (n-7)\,H_2O$$
$$\rightleftarrows Mg(H_2O)_{n-x}^{+2}(aq) + SO_4(H_2O)_x^{-2}(aq) \qquad +\Delta H_2 \quad (2)$$

We note that the products of reactions (1) and (2) are identical, i.e., there is formed a mole of magnesium ions and a mole of sulfate ions in a liter volume of aqueous solution. The striking difference between these reactions is that for reaction (1) the enthalpy change is negative, while for reaction (2) it is positive. The basis for this difference is due entirely to the hydration, or solvation, of the small, positively charged magnesium ions by water molecules. Thus, although a positive enthalpy accompanies the rupture of the solid crystalline lattice,

2

a process which must take place for dissolution of both solid compounds, the negative enthalpy which accompanies the hydration of the magnesium ions when the anhydrous compound is dissolved is more than sufficient to overcome the positive enthalpy terms. Since the free energy of solution is largely determined by the enthalpy of solution, the hydration energy term plays a major role in determining the solubility of a compound.

The ability of water to dissolve different compounds varies a great deal. Its inability to dissolve certain substances together with the need to get materials into solution, creates an interest in solvents other than water. Thus, silver iodide, which is virtually insoluble in water, is exceedingly soluble in liquid ammonia, and the alkali metals, which react violently with water, dissolve in liquid ammonia to give concentrated solutions of these metals. The dissolution of alkali metals in liquid ammonia, of considerable theoretical interest, is a very useful tool for use in synthesis, especially in the preparation of alkali metal-organic derivatives, and in other reactions in which controlled reduction is required. We shall deal with several of these uses subsequently.

One of the most important properties which determines the solvent properties of a liquid is the *dielectric constant* (see Sec. 1–C), and this quantity is, in turn, related to the *dipole moment*. Water possesses an unusually large dielectric constant which results from its unusually large dipole moment and its strongly hydrogen bonded structure. Thus, water is an unusually good solvent for ionic solids which dissociate into ions upon solution, e.g., typical salts, but is a poor solvent for many covalent solids, e.g., mercurous chloride and nonpolar organic compounds.

One of the most important properties of water is its self-dissociation into hydrated protons, or *hydronium* ions, and hydrated hydroxide ions. This autoionization may be written as

$$(n + 1)\, H_2O + H_2O \rightleftarrows H_3O^+ + [OH \cdot n(H_2O)]^- \qquad (3)$$

Although this equation is the correct one, for simplicity and ease in writing we will write this reaction as

$$2\, H_2O \rightleftarrows H_3O^+ + OH^-{}^* \qquad (4)$$

---

* The exact stoichiometry of the hydrated proton species is not a matter of established fact. For this reason, in accordance with established convention, the hydrated proton will be designated as H_3O^+.

The most significant implication of this autoionization reaction is that in water, the strongest acid which may exist is the proton and the strongest base which may exist is the hydroxide ion. Thus, when a familiar base such as sodium hydroxide is added to water, it dissolves as follows

$$NaOH(s) \rightarrow Na^+(aq) + OH^-(aq) \tag{5}$$

In water, sodium hydroxide is a strong base. If we dissolve hydrogen chloride in water, it dissolves as follows

$$HCl(g) \rightarrow H^+(aq) + Cl^-(aq) \tag{6}$$

and is a strong acid since the ionization is essentially quantitative. However, if we should be interested in comparing the relative acidities of strong acids such as H_2SO_4, HNO_3, HCl, etc., the equilibrium constants in water are always found to be too large, i.e., the dissociation in water is essentially 100 percent and such a comparison cannot be made.

We could discuss at length the limitations imposed upon us by restricting scientific investigations entirely to reactions in water. There is no doubt that water will always be the most important solvent and it is a most remarkable substance. However, interesting new chemistry has been and is being discovered by studying reactions in solvents other than water. Let us now look further into this subject.

1–C   CLASSIFICATION OF SOLVENTS

A number of different classifications, based primarily upon experimental results, has been suggested for nonaqueous solvents. It will soon become evident that no single classification is adequate. The choice of a particular classification will depend almost entirely upon the solvent under consideration, i.e., that classification will be utilized which most adequately describes the properties of a particular solvent.

Inasmuch as the solubility of substances and the chemical reactions which take place in various solvents depends to a very great degree upon the dielectric constant of the solvent, an understanding of the meaning of this term is very much in order.

When two electric charges, e_1 and e_2, are a distance r apart in a uniform medium, the size of the force F which exists between these charges is determined by the inherent physical property of the medium which we call the dielectric constant, D. This force is given by Coulomb's law as

$$F = \frac{e_1 e_2}{D r^2}$$

The interesting aspect of this relationship is that if e_1 and e_2 are of opposite charge, the force of attraction between e_1 and e_2 *decreases* as the dielectric constant increases. In recognition of the fact that strong coulombic forces exist among the charged particles which make up ionic crystals, we are able to predict that the higher the dielectric constant of a given solvent, the greater its ability is to dissolve ionic solids. This is true because of the ability of a solvent of high dielectric constant to overcome the strong ionic forces binding the particles that make up ionic crystals. However, not all solvents of high dielectric constant are good solvents for ionic substances. For example, HCN, with a dielectric constant of ca. 115, is a poor solvent for ionic substances. This is largely because of its inability to coordinate ions strongly. The importance of the latter property will be discussed subsequently.

Two principal factors which determine the dielectric constant are the *dipole moment* and *hydrogen bonding*. As mentioned previously, water, which possesses a large dipole moment and which is very strongly hydrogen bonded, has an unusually high dielectric constant. In Table 1 are listed some common solvents and the values of their dielectric constants at specified temperatures. The value of the dielectric constant, itself, can be used as a basis for the classification of solvents. When a chemist refers to water as "a solvent of high dielectric constant" or to phosgene as a "medium of low dielectric constant," these statements convey a very definite meaning.

An extremely important physical process which helps us to understand the solubility of ionic crystals and the stability of solutions of electrolytes in solvents of high dielectric constant is the solvation of ions.

Every ion, because it is a charged particle, creates about itself an electric field. Because of this the dipoles of the solvent molecule will orient themselves about the ion. This is known as *ion-dipole* attraction. Since the field about an ion is proportional to the charge on the ion and inversely proportional to the size of the ion, it logically follows that small, highly charged ions and solvent molecules having high dipole moments will have the strongest attraction for one

Table 1

*Dielectric Constants of Various Solvents
at Specified Temperatures*

Solvent	Dielectric Constant, D	(°C)
Water	88.0	0
Ammonia	23	−33
	18.94	5
	16.90	25
Hydrogen fluoride	175	−73
	84	0
Hydrogen chloride	9.28	−95
Hydrogen bromide	7.0	−85
Hydrogen iodide	3.39	−50
Sulfuric acid	100	25
Acetic acid	6	25
Sulfur dioxide	15.4	0.25
Arsenic trichloride	12.6	17
Arsenic tribromide	8.8	35
Antimony trichloride	33.0	75
Antimony tribromide	20.9	100
Phosphorus oxytrichloride	13.9	22
Pyridine	12.5	20
Phosgene	4.34	22

another. These forces may be strong enough to allow the existence of stable, solid solvates, e.g., $Fe(NO_3)_3 \cdot 6\,H_2O$, $KF \cdot 3\,HF$, and $Na_2Zn(C_2H_3O_2)_4 \cdot 4\,HC_2H_3O_2$. In solvents having low dielectric constants, such as the hydrocarbons, carbon tetrachloride, etc., the solvent-solute interactions are not strong enough to overcome the coulombic forces which exist in ionic crystals and hence they are poor solvents for electrolytes.

A useful classification which has emerged from the Brönsted-Lowry concept of acids and bases (to be discussed in the next chapter) is based upon the *protophylic* character of the solvent, i.e., its tendency to donate or accept protons. Utilizing this concept, a solvent will fall into one of four types. Those which are strong proton donors such as perchloric, nitric, sulfuric, and acetic acids are classified as *acidic solvents*. Those solvents which are proton acceptors, such as ammonia, hydrazine, and amines are classified as *basic solvents*. Water and hydroxylic compounds, such as the lower molecular weight alcohols, which may function either as proton donors or proton acceptors are classified as *amphoteric solvents* or as *amphiprotic*. Finally, many solvents, especially those which possess very low dielectric constants, such as the hydrocarbons and carbon tetrachloride, are essentially inactive with respect to proton transfer. These fall into the category of *aprotic solvents*.

Another concept which has been widely used for classification is that of *parent solvents*. In this view the solvent is regarded as the parent of a derived system of acids, bases, and salts which are logically related to the parent. Thus, the parent solvent, water, gives rise to hydronium ions, H_3O^+, hydroxide ions, OH^-, and oxide ions, O^{-2}. In an analogous manner, the parent solvent, ammonia, gives rise to ammonium ions, NH_4^+, and amide, imide, and nitride ions, NH_2^-, NH^{-2}, and N^{-3}. This analogy can be extended to many other solvents and has found a great deal of practical application, especially in predicting the nature of the chemical reactions which may be expected to take place in a given solvent.

When typical mineral acids such as hydrochloric, sulfuric, nitric, perchloric, etc., are dissolved in water, they all behave as very strong acids. This means that at comparable concentrations they are ionized to the same degree, i.e., they yield essentially equal concentrations of hydronium ion. Water is thus described as a *leveling* solvent toward these acids. In acetic acid, however, the acid strengths of the common mineral acids vary considerably. There exists a marked difference in the degree of dissociation as observed from conductivity measurements. Acetic acid has the ability to differentiate among them and is called a *differentiating solvent*. There are many factors which determine electrolyte strength and these factors play different roles to varying degrees in different solvents. Hence, a classification based upon electrolyte strength, while useful, is quite limited.

Many other schemes of classification have been presented and discussion of all of them is not possible. The foregoing are the main ones and will be utilized throughout this presentation.

Exercises

1. How is the dielectric constant measured experimentally?
2. How is the dielectric constant related to the dipole moment?
3. Sketch a Born-Haber type cycle for the energy changes involved in the dissolution of a salt.

4. Discuss the relationship between crystal energy and aqueous solubility.
5. Arrange the following ions in order of their increasing negative enthalpies of hydration: Ca^{+2}, Ba^{+2}, Zn^{+2}, Al^{+3}, Fe^{+3}, F^-, I^-, Cs^+, Na^+.

References

1. A. E. Van Arkel, *Molecules and Crystals*, Interscience, 1949.
2. T. C. Waddington, *Lattice Energies*, in "Advances in Inorganic Chemistry and Radiochemistry," H. J. Emeléus and A. G. Sharpe, Eds., Vol. I, Academic Press, 1959.
3. J. A. A. Ketelaar, *Chemical Constitution*, Elsevier, 1958, Ch. 11.
4. J. H. Hildebrand and R. L. Scott, *The Solubility of Non-Electrolytes*, Dover, 1964, Ch. IX.
5. R. J. W. LeFevre, *Dipole Moments*, Methuen, 1953.

CHAPTER **2**

*Acids and Bases and Some Theories Dealing with
the Behavior of Solutes in Nonaqueous Solvents*

2–A THE ARRHENIUS THEORY OF ACIDS AND BASES

To this day there exists no unanimous agreement as to what properly characterizes and constitutes an acid. Although significant theories on this subject had been put forth before 1885, the present discussion will begin with the well-known theory presented by Arrhenius during that year. The experimental background which furnished the foundation for this theory was the study of the behavior of electrolytes in aqueous solutions. When it became generally recognized that certain substances, such as hydrogen chloride, which were nonconductors in the pure liquid state, became strong electrolytes upon dissolution in water, it was logically concluded that the solvent played a highly significant role. Arrhenius pointed out that the electrical conductivity data, which had been gathered for aqueous solutions, could be interpreted if it were assumed that complete dissociation into the constituent ions took place at infinite dilution for all dissolved salts. A gradual decrease in the extent of this dissociation with increasing salt concentration was proposed.

According to the Arrhenius theory of acids and bases, an acid is a hydrogen-containing compound, which, upon dissolution in water, gives a solution containing hydrogen ions; a base is any hydroxyl-bearing compound, which, when dissolved in water, yields a solution containing hydroxide ions. This simple concept was extremely useful in furnishing an explanation for a number of phenomena which had

9

been puzzling chemists for many years.   For instance, the constant value which had been observed for the heat of neutralization of any strong base by any strong acid could be readily interpreted in terms of the formation of water by a proton-hydroxide ion reaction, since the hydrogen ion is common to solutions of all strong acids and the hydroxide ion to solutions of all strong bases.   For aqueous solutions, the acid-base theory of Arrhenius is quite adequate.   Among the several objections raised to it is the fact that it is limited to the solvent, water.   It does not, for example, explain the acid behavior of ammonium salts in liquid ammonia.   While the historic importance and great utility of the Arrhenius concept for water systems is not to be underestimated, let us consider some additional ideas which broaden and extend our concepts of acids and bases.

2–B   THE BRÖNSTED-LOWRY THEORY OF ACIDS AND BASES

An extension of the Arrhenius theory was proposed almost concurrently (1923) by Brönsted in Denmark and by Lowry in England. In their view, an acid is defined as a proton donor and a base as a proton acceptor.   This concept immediately extends the definition of "acid" and "base" beyond the limits imposed by the Arrhenius theory.   It is probable that you have observed in the laboratory the formation of dense fumes of ammonium chloride which form when a bottle of ammonia and a bottle of hydrochloric acid are opened in the vicinity of one another.   The equation for this reaction may be written

$$NH_3(g) + HCl(g) \rightarrow NH_4Cl(s)$$

This reaction cannot be an acid-base reaction in the Arrhenius sense since it does not take place in water, but it is in the Brönsted-Lowry sense as we shall see.

The fundamental relationships suggested by the Brönsted concept are given by

$$acid_1 \rightleftarrows H^+ + base_1 \tag{1}$$

$$base_2 + H^+ \rightleftarrows acid_2 \tag{2}$$

An acid is thus defined as a *proton donor* and a base as a *proton acceptor*.   Summation of equations (1) and (2) gives

$$acid_1 + base_2 \rightleftarrows base_1 + acid_2 \tag{3}$$

10

According to this view, any acid-base reaction involves two acids and two bases and the combination of acid and its derivative base is called a *conjugate pair*. Thus, dry hydrogen chloride gas can be described as an acid in accordance with equation (1), i.e.,

$$HCl \rightleftarrows H^+ + Cl^-$$

However, anhydrous hydrogen chloride does not function as an acid, i.e., it does not give up its proton, until it comes in contact with a base that is a stronger proton acceptor than is the chloride ion. Since ammonia *is* a stronger base than chloride ion, proton transfer occurs and we write the reaction

$$HCl + NH_3 \rightleftarrows NH_4^+ + Cl^-$$
$$acid_1 \quad base_2 \quad acid_2 \quad base_1$$

When a hydrogen halide gas is dissolved in water, the water molecule acts as a base in the Brönsted sense. The halide ion, X^-, is the conjugate base of the acid, HX, and the hydronium ion, H_3O^+, is the conjugate acid of the base, water. Thus, the ionization of hydrogen halides in water solution can be written in the Brönsted view as follows

$$HX + H_2O \rightarrow H_3O^+ + X^-$$
$$acid_1 \quad base_2 \quad acid_2 \quad base_1$$

Salts of weak acids, such as acetates, carbonates and cyanides, when dissolved in water, act as proton acceptors, e.g.,

$$H_2O + CN^- \rightleftarrows HCN + OH^-$$
$$acid_1 \quad base_2 \quad acid_2 \quad base_1$$

The scope of the Brönsted theory is further illustrated by the reaction of toluene with sodium methyl, in hydrocarbon solvents, viz.,

$$C_6H_5CH_3 + NaCH_3 \rightarrow C_6H_5CH_2^-Na^+ + CH_4$$

In this reaction, the base, methide ion, (CH_3^-) accepts a proton from the acid, toluene.

Whether a given species behaves as an acid or as a base in a given reaction will depend upon the relative acidity of the other reactant. Consider the ionization of carbonic acid

$$H_2CO_3 \rightleftarrows H^+ + HCO_3^-$$
$$HCO_3^- \rightleftarrows H^+ + CO_3^{-2}$$

11

In the presence of the hydroxide ion, which is a stronger base than the bicarbonate ion, the bicarbonate ion acts as an acid by donating a proton to the OH^-,

$$HCO_3^- + OH^- \rightleftarrows CO_3^{-2} + H_2O$$

When a strong acid, e.g., aqueous nitric acid, is added to a solution of bicarbonate ion, the latter acts as a base since it becomes a proton acceptor

$$HCO_3^- + H^+ \rightleftarrows H_2CO_3$$

Another important consideration which is introduced by the Brönsted theory is the vital role which is played by the solvent. Urea, while it behaves as an acid in liquid ammonia, functions as a base in formic acid. These types of behavior may be illustrated by

$$
\begin{array}{cccc}
(NH_2)_2CO + & NH_3 & \rightleftarrows H_2NC(O)NH^- + & NH_4^+ \\
\text{acid}_1 & \text{base}_2 & \text{base}_1 & \text{acid}_2 \\
HCOOH + (NH_2)_2CO \rightleftarrows & & HCOO^- & + H_2NC(O)NH_3^+
\end{array}
$$

Similarly, acetic acid, which is a Brönsted acid in water, behaves as a base in liquid hydrogen fluoride

$$
\begin{array}{cccc}
CH_3COOH + & HF & \rightleftarrows CH_3COOH_2^+ + & F^- \\
\text{base}_1 & \text{acid}_2 & \text{acid}_1 & \text{base}_2
\end{array}
$$

The Brönsted-Lowry definitions extend our concept of acids and bases well beyond the limits imposed by the Arrhenius theory. The limitations in each case are imposed by the definitions upon which the theory is based. Under the Brönsted theory the proton becomes the ultimate factor in acid-base considerations. We will find even this definition to be too restrictive since many acid-base reactions have been shown to take place without proton transfer.

2–C   THE THEORY OF SOLVENT SYSTEMS OR IONOTROPY

A significant extension of the acid-base concept which includes non-protonic as well as protonic solvents was developed during the early part of this century. It grew largely out of the pioneering studies of E. C. Franklin, H. P. Cady, and C. A. Kraus which were concerned with reactions in liquid ammonia. Franklin pointed out that remarkable analogies exist between the water and the ammonia systems. The autoionization of water into hydronium and hydroxide ions is paralleled by the ionization of liquid ammonia into ammonium and amide ions,

$$2\,H_2O \rightleftarrows H_3O^+ + OH^-$$
$$2\,NH_3 \rightleftarrows NH_4^+ + NH_2^-$$

Similarly, a neutralization reaction in water (the reaction between the hydroxide and hydronium ions to form the solvent) is paralleled by the reaction between ammonium and amide ions to form ammonia,

$$NaOH\ +\ HCl\ \rightarrow NaCl + H_2O$$
$$NaNH_2 + NH_4Cl \rightarrow NaCl + 2\,NH_3$$
$$\text{base}\qquad \text{acid}\qquad \text{salt}\qquad \text{solvent}$$

This concept of solvent systems was soon extended, not only to other protonic solvents, but to nonprotonic solvents as well. The generalized definition of the solvent system theory as stated by Cady and Elsey is essentially as follows: *an acid is a solute which, upon dissolution, yields cations characteristic of the solvent either by direct dissociation or by reaction with the solvent; a base is a solute which yields anions characteristic of the solvent either by direct dissociation in or by reaction with the solvent.* This concept can be further extended to include the definition of neutralization as *the reaction between cations and anions characteristic of the solvent to form solvent molecules.* Let us list a series of solvents showing the cations and anions characteristic of each and describe typical neutralization reactions according to the solvent system theory:

Solvent	*Cation*	*Anion*	*Neutralization Reaction*
$HC_2H_3O_2$	$H_2C_2H_3O_2^+$	$C_2H_3O_2^-$	$HNO_3 + KC_2H_3O_2$ $\rightarrow KNO_3 + HC_2H_3O_2$
SO_2	SO^{+2}	SO_3^{-2}	$SOCl_2 + Cs_2SO_3$ $\rightarrow 2\,SO_2 + 2\,CsCl$
$COCl_2$	$COCl^+$	Cl^-	$2\,COCl^+ + 2\,AlCl_4^-$ $+\ Ca^{+2} + 2\,Cl^-$ $\rightarrow Ca(AlCl_4)_2 + 2\,COCl_2$

(By reaction of a solution of aluminum chloride in phosgene with one of calcium chloride in the same solvent.)

13

Solvent	Cation	Anion	Neutralization Reaction
BrF_3	BrF_2^+	BrF_4^-	$BrF_2NbF_6 + KBrF_4$ $\rightarrow KNbF_6 + 2\, BrF_3$
HCN	H_2CN^+	CN^-	$H_2SO_4 + KCN$ $\rightarrow KHSO_4 + HCN$

The basic objection which has been raised to the theory of solvent-systems is that it omits many acid-base reactions as they are defined by the protonic (Brönsted-Lowry) theory. In a sense, it represents an extension of the Arrhenius theory to each individual solvent. It does, however, extend the acid-base concept to systems which would otherwise not be included under the two theories previously discussed.

2–D   THE LEWIS CONCEPT

At about the same time that the Brönsted-Lowry theory was proposed, one of the most famous of all American chemists, G. N. Lewis, presented what is considered by many to be the most basic and inclusive concept of acids and bases. It is frequently termed the electronic theory and defines an acid as an *electron pair acceptor* and a base as an *electron pair donor*. The neutralization process is described as the formation of a coordinate covalent bond as the result of electron pair donation by the base to the acid. According to this definition, any chemical reaction involving the formation of a coordinate covalent bond in the classical sense would fall into the realm of acid-base reactions. As soon as we examine those substances which may be classified as Lewis acids and bases we begin to appreciate just how broad this theory is.

The proton is a Lewis acid because it seeks an electron pair, as, for example, in the formation of the ammonium ion or of the hydronium ion,

$$H^+ + \; :\!\overset{\displaystyle H}{\underset{\displaystyle H}{\overset{..}{N}}}\!: H \rightleftharpoons H:\overset{\displaystyle H}{\underset{\displaystyle H}{\overset{..}{N}}}:H \;\;^+$$

$$H^+ + \; :\!\overset{\displaystyle H}{\underset{}{\overset{..}{O}}}\!: H \rightleftharpoons H:\overset{\displaystyle H}{\underset{}{\overset{..}{O}}}:H \;\;^+$$

14

Positive ions form a typical group of Lewis acids. Reactions which form complex ions, such as $[(Ag(CN)_2]^-$ and $[Cu(NH_3)_4]^{+2}$, represent Lewis acid-base reactions,

$$Ag^+ + 2 : CN : ^- \rightleftarrows [Ag(: CN :)_2]^-$$
$$Cu^{+2} + 4 : NH_3 \rightleftarrows [Cu(: NH_3)_4]^{+2}$$

Addition compounds which are formed by reactions of molecules containing unfilled octets with molecules, anions, or atoms having unshared electron pairs, fall into the realm of Lewis acid-base reactions

$$
\begin{array}{c}
\text{CH}_3 \quad \text{Cl} \qquad\qquad \text{H}_3\text{C} \quad \text{Cl} \\
| \qquad\quad | \qquad\qquad\qquad | \qquad\quad | \\
\text{H}_3\text{C} : \text{As} : \; + \; \text{B} : \text{Cl} \rightarrow \text{CH}_3 : \text{As} : \text{B} : \text{Cl} \\
| \qquad\quad | \qquad\qquad\qquad | \qquad\quad | \\
\text{CH}_3 \quad \text{Cl} \qquad\qquad \text{H}_3\text{C} \quad \text{Cl}
\end{array}
$$

$$
\begin{array}{c}
\qquad\quad \text{F} \qquad\quad \text{F} \quad {}^- \\
\;\; .. \quad {}^- \qquad | \qquad\quad | \\
: \text{F} : \quad + \; \text{B} : \text{F} \rightarrow \text{F} : \text{B} : \text{F} \\
\;\; .. \qquad\qquad | \qquad\quad | \\
\qquad\quad \text{F} \qquad\quad \text{F}
\end{array}
$$

$$
\begin{array}{c}
\text{R} \qquad\qquad\qquad \text{R} \\
| \qquad\quad .. \qquad\quad | \qquad\quad .. \\
\text{R} : \text{Sb} : \; + \cdot \text{S} : \; \rightarrow \text{R} : \text{Sb} : \text{S} : \\
| \qquad\quad \cdot \qquad\quad | \qquad\quad .. \\
\text{R} \qquad\qquad\qquad \text{R}
\end{array}
$$

Amines, alcohols, thioethers, selenoureas, etc., are all Lewis bases since the N, O, S, and Se atoms can behave as electron pair donors.

Before leaving the Lewis theory, it is desirable to enumerate the four basic experimental criteria which the theory establishes as characteristic of acids and bases. These are:

1. *Neutralization*—The formation of a covalent bond between acids and bases is a rapid process and may be followed by ionization.

2. *Displacement reactions*—A given acid or base will displace a weaker acid or base from its compounds. For example, ammonia, a stronger base than water, will convert the hydronium ion, H_3O^+, to water with the formation of the ammonium ion, NH_4^+.

3. *Titration reactions*—Acids and bases may be titrated against one another in the presence of indicators, usually colored. This property enables us to follow the degree of completion of the reaction. Titrations do not necessarily require the presence of hydrogen ion.

4. *Catalysis*—Both acids and bases are characterized by their ability to function as catalysts and thereby accelerate many chemical reactions.

If there is a single general criticism of the Lewis theory it is that the theory is so broad that too many chemical reactions fall into the category of the acid-base type.

2–E   THE USANOVICH THEORY

Several other definitions of acids and bases have been proposed, but since they have found neither a great deal of acceptance nor utility, only one of them, the *Usanovich* definition, will be mentioned. Usanovich defined an acid as *any species which produces cations, is able to combine with anions or electrons, or which is able to form a salt when neutralized by a base. A base is defined as any substance which gives up anions or electrons, or which is able to combine with cations.* It can be readily seen that this theory is even broader than that of Lewis. It includes as acids or bases all of the substances which are so classified in all of the other concepts and adds oxidizing and reducing agents. This theory is so very broad that virtually all chemical reactions become acid-base reactions and it really obviates the need for any acid-base classification since the term "chemical reaction" would suffice.

2–F   THE COORDINATION MODEL FOR THE BEHAVIOR OF SOLUTES IN NONAQUEOUS SOLVENTS

The coordination model is not an acid-base theory, but a general theory which attempts to describe solute behavior in nonaqueous solvents. It is due to R. S. Drago and co-workers, and details may be found in several recent articles by that investigator.

The essence of the concept is that the donor (or acceptor) strength of a solvent molecule and its ability to solvate the dissolved species are the primary factors which determine what the nature of the solute species in solution will be. Upon dissolution of a solute, MX_n, in a solvent, S, the first step, assuming S to be a Lewis type donor molecule, is a Lewis type acid-base interaction given by the equilibrium

$$MX_n + p\ S \rightleftarrows MX_nS_p$$

If the X groups are coordinated to M, MX_nS_p is an adduct of the Lewis type. If the groups, X, bonded to M are anionic in nature, these groups can be displaced by solvent molecules as

$$MS_pX_n + S \rightleftarrows (MS_{p+1}X_{n-1})^+ + X^-$$
$$(MS_{p+1}X_{n-1})^+ + S \rightleftarrows (MS_{p+2}X_{n-2})^{+2} + X^-, \text{ etc.}$$

The extent to which the anions are replaced by solvent molecules depends upon the thermodynamics of the interactions. In order to apply the coordination model it is essential to have structural and thermodynamic information about the addition compound and the subsequent reactions which it undergoes.

A basic thermochemical cycle can be written to describe the enthalpy contributions to the equilibria which involve the dissolution of a polar covalent compound MX and all of the species formed by its reactions. If the assumption is made that the compound and all species derived from it are soluble and that the coordination number does not change, then the basic equilibrium is described by the equation

$$S \ (solv) + S_pMX_n \ (solv) \rightleftarrows [S_{p+1}MX_{n-1}]^+ \ (solv) + X^- \ (solv)$$

A thermochemical cycle which is based upon this equilibrium and which describes the fundamental enthalpies involved can be written

$$
\begin{array}{cccccc}
MS_pX_n(g) & + & S(g) & \xrightarrow{c} & MS_{p+1}X_{n-1}^+(g) & + & X^-(g) \\
\uparrow a & & \uparrow b & & \downarrow d & & \downarrow e \\
MS_pX_n \ (solv) & + & S \ (solv) & \rightleftarrows & MS_{p+1}X_{n-1}^+ \ (solv) & + & X^- \ (solv)
\end{array}
$$

where the enthalpy contributions which affect this equilibrium are determined by

1. the enthalpy of solvation of S (g) Step b
2. the difference in the enthalpies of solvation of
   $MS_pX_n(g)$ and $MS_{p+1}X_{n-1}^+(g)$ (Step d)–(Step a)
3. the solvation of $X^-(g)$ Step e
4. the difference in donor strengths of $X^-(g)$
   and $S(g)$ Step c.

In order to avoid later difficulty some of the terms employed by Drago should be defined. *Donor* and *acceptor* strength are measures of the enthalpy of a donor-acceptor interaction measured in the *absence* of solvation. *Basicity* or *acidity* refer specifically to an equilibrium constant either pK_a or pK_b measured in a solvating solvent. *Specific solvation* refers specifically to a solute-solvent Lewis acid-base inter-action *beyond the first coordination sphere. Nonspecific solvation* is a term reserved for dipolar interactions beyond the first coordination sphere, but which are *not* of the Lewis acid-base type, i.e., they are primarily dipole-dipole interactions.

A considerably greater number of simplifying requirements and assumptions are needed, and to quote the authors (ref. 1) "an exact knowledge of the enthalpy and the entropy changes which accompany the steps in the energy cycles for different solvents would lead to a clear understanding of the dependence of the position of the equi-librium on the principal solvent properties. Unfortunately, in the case of solutes that ionize, the enthalpies for several of the steps cannot be measured at present. Enthalpies corresponding to steps (c) and (d) plus (e) are impossible to obtain for most systems, and step (a) usually is impossible to measure. As a result a rigorous solu-tion to this problem is not possible at present."

Let us examine the behavior of $FeCl_3$ in $PO(OEt)_3$ as described by the coordination model. The first step involves formation of a Lewis acid-base adduct between ferric chloride (Lewis acid) and the phosphate (donor solvent molecule), which then dissociates to give a chloride ion and the solvate coordinated cation.

$$FeCl_3 + n\ OPR_3 \rightleftarrows FeCl_3(OPR_3)_n \rightleftarrows (R_3PO)_nFeCl_2^+ + Cl^-$$

$$(R = OEt)$$

The adduct may also react with the chloride ion to form tetra-chloroferrate ion and free phosphate

$$FeCl_3(OPR_3)_n + Cl^- \rightleftarrows (OPR_3)_{n-1}FeCl_4^- + R_3PO$$

Additional stepwise replacement of anions by solvent molecules is shown by the reactions

$$OPR_3 + FeCl_2(OPR_3)_n^+ \rightleftarrows FeCl(OPR_3)_{n+1}^{+2} + Cl^-$$
$$OPR_3 + FeCl(OPR_3)_{n+1} \rightleftarrows Fe(OPR_3)_{n+2}^{+3} + Cl^-$$

The coordination model is currently receiving considerable atten-tion, but whether sufficient experimental data will be accumulated to put it to a quantitative test remains to be seen. Solvation, in those solvents in which it does take place, is essentially an acid-base reac-tion in the Lewis sense.

In conclusion we may say that the utility and application of any acid-base theory is largely a matter of definition. As Humpty-Dumpty said in Lewis Carroll's *Through the Looking Glass*, "When I use a word it means just what I choose it to mean—neither more nor less."

Exercises

1. A solution of ammonium sulfate in liquid ammonia is treated with a solution of sodium amide in liquid ammonia. Write a balanced equation for the probable reaction. Interpret this reaction according to the Brönsted, Lewis, and solvent system concepts.
2. Examine the literature and discuss the acid-base theories of Lux-Flood, Ebert-Konopik, Bjerrum, and Mulliken (see refs. 5–8). Criticize each in terms of novelty and utility.
3. When perchloric acid is dissolved in anhydrous sulfuric acid it ionizes to give ClO_4^- and $H_3SO_4^+$. What role does sulfuric acid fulfill in the acid-base sense?
4. Is each of the following a Brönsted acid, a Brönsted base, or both: Se^{-2}, PH_3, NH_2^-, CN^-, HPO_4^{-2}, D_2O, pyridine, HCO_3^-, $Fe(H_2O)_6^{+3}$?
5. Is each of the following a Lewis acid, a Lewis base, or neither: $AsCl_3$, pyridine, acetaldehyde, NH_3, BF_4^-, Hg^{+2}, Cl^-, $(CH_3)_2C{=}Se$, pentadiene, pentadienide ion?

References

1. R. S. Drago and K. F. Purcell, *Progress in Inorganic Chemistry*, Vol. 6, Interscience, 1964; Ch. 5 of *Nonaqueous Solvent Systems*, T. C. Waddington, Ed., Academic, 1965.
2. L. F. Audrieth and J. Kleinberg, *Nonaqueous Solvents*, Wiley, 1953.
3. R. P. Bell, *Acids and Bases*, Methuen, 1952.
4. W. Luder and S. Zuffanti, *The Electronic Theory of Acids and Bases*, Wiley, 1946.
5. H. Lux, *Z. Electrochem.*, **45,** 303 (1939).
6. H. Flood, T. Foerland, and B. Roald, *Acta. Chem. Scand.*, **1,** 790 (1947).
7. L. Ebert and N. Konopik, "Acidity and Basicity," *Oesterr. Chem.-Ztg.*, **50,** 184 (1949).
8. N. Bjerrum, "Acids, Salts, and Bases," *Chem. Revs.*, **16,** 287 (1935).

CHAPTER **3**

Liquid Ammonia as a Solvent

3–A SOME PROBLEMS WHICH MUST BE SOLVED WHEN WORKING WITH NONAQUEOUS SOLVENTS

The nature of some of the solvents in which experimental work has been performed is such that the investigator is faced with a number of technical problems as well as some concerning health and safety. Among the more widely studied nonaqueous solvents are ammonia, hydrogen fluoride, sulfur dioxide, hydrogen cyanide, phosgene and molten salts such as potassium fluoride. In addition to dealing with toxicological problems, the investigator must concern himself with the purity of his materials if meaningful and accurate experimental data are to be obtained. Since many of these substances are extremely sensitive to moisture, an atmosphere free of water vapor must be provided. In addition, many of these compounds assume the liquid state only at relatively low, or relatively high temperatures. For example, the normal boiling point of liquid ammonia is −33°C. Under ordinary laboratory conditions it becomes necessary to provide external cooling such as would be furnished by a Dry Ice-acetone mixture.

A substance like hydrogen fluoride readily attacks not only siliceous materials including glass and stoneware, but a number of metals. Thus, when working with this corrosive solvent it is necessary to use vessels made of stainless steel, copper, or an inert plastic such as polyethylene, teflon, or Kel-F.

Another interesting group of solvents which has been studied during recent years consists of molten salts such as potassium nitrate and molten fluorides, the latter in connection with the construction of a new type of nuclear reactor, MSRE (Molten Salt Reactor). In this case, it becomes necessary to supply enough external energy to fuse these salts and to maintain them at temperatures above their melting points while they are under investigation. Containers which are resistant to chemical attack by these substances at high temperatures must also be found. In addition, thermocouples, electrodes, and other devices which are needed to make fundamental physical measurements must be specially designed to meet the unusual experimental conditions.

3–B   AMMONIA AND HYDROGEN FLUORIDE AS SOLVENTS— GENERAL CONSIDERATIONS

Two solvents which are worthy of some detailed examination are ammonia and hydrogen fluoride. The former has been the subject of a great deal of detailed investigation while the latter furnishes several illustrations of how research in nonaqueous solvent systems may yield results of great practical importance. Both are *protonic* solvents, one basic and the other acidic, and both present challenging experimental problems which had to be solved before meaningful and successful investigations could be performed. Liquid ammonia and liquid hydrogen fluoride are referred to as "water-like" solvents since they associated through hydrogen bonding, possess high dielectric constants, and exist in the liquid state over a relatively wide temperature range.

In Table 3–1 are listed the more commonly used physical constants for water, ammonia, and hydrogen fluoride.

Among the pioneers in the field of liquid ammonia chemistry must be included A. Joannis, E. C. Franklin, C. A. Kraus, and H. P. Cady. The work of Joannis, carried on during the last decade of the 19th century, unfortunately has not received the recognition to which it is entitled. The work of the other three began during the late 1890's and continued, uninterrupted, for many years. Their efforts led to the training of a school of liquid ammonia chemists, some of whom continue their activities in this field today. Most of the laboratory techniques currently utilized in this field of research were developed by these men and their students. As a result of their work, liquid ammonia has become a widely used solvent in both organic and inorganic chemistry.

Table 3–1

Some Physical Properties of
Water, Ammonia, and Hydrogen Fluoride

Physical Constant	H_2O	NH_3	HF
Molecular Weight	18.016	17.032	20.008
Density (grams/ml)	0.958 (100°)	0.683 (−33.4°)	0.991 (19.5°)
Molecular volume (ml)	18.8	24.9	20.8
Melting point (°C)	0	−77.7	−83.1
Boiling point (°C)	100	−33.4	19.54
Critical temperature (°C)	374.1	132.4	230.2
Critical pressure (atm)	217.7	112	
Heat of fusion (kcal/mole)	1.435	1.43	1.094
Heat of vapn. (kcal/mole)	9.719	5.64	7.24
Equiv. cond. (ohm^{-1})	6×10^{-8} (25°)	5×10^{-9} (−33.4°)	1.4×10^{-5}
Dielectric constant	81.1 (18°)	22 (−34°)	83.6 (0°)
Viscosity (dyne sec/cm^2)	0.00959 (25°)	0.00265 (−33.5°)	
Molecular f.p. constant (°C/1000 grams)	1.859	0.97	
Molecular b.p. constant (°C/1000 grams)	0.51	0.34	
Dipole Moment ($D \times 10^{18}$)	1.85	1.47	1.9

Every student of chemistry has been exposed to ammonia fumes and is acutely aware of the fact that they cause severe physiological reactions. Not only because of its obvious toxicity, but also because of its low boiling point, operations with liquid ammonia must be carried out in a hood, or better, in a closed system. Ammonia of high purity is commercially available. Moisture can be removed very efficiently, when this is necessary, by dissolving metallic sodium, which reacts irreversibly with water, directly in the liquid. Dry ammonia can be distilled from this solution.

3–C   SOLUBILITY OF METALS IN LIQUID AMMONIA

One of the most remarkable properties of liquid ammonia is its ability to dissolve alkali metals freely to give relatively stable solutions. These metals, of course, react violently and irreversibly with water. The solubilities of lithium, sodium, and potassium *exceed one mole per 100 g of liquid ammonia* at −33°C (Table 3–2). These solubilities are much higher than those of salts such as sodium chloride or sodium sulfate in water. Evaporation of the solutions leads to recovery of unreacted metal. The alkaline earth metals are also soluble, but to a much smaller degree than the alkali metals.

Table 3–2

Solubilities of Alkali Metals in Liquid Ammonia

Metal	T(°C)	Gram-atoms of metal per 1000 g NH_3	Moles NH_3 per gram-atom of metal
Lithium	0	16.31	3.60
	−33.2	15.66	3.75
	−39.4	16.25	3.61
	−63.5	15.41	3.81
Sodium	22	9.56	6.14
	0	10.00	5.87
	−30	10.63	5.52
	−33.8	10.72	5.48
	−33.5	10.93	5.37
	−50	10.89	5.39
	−70	11.29	5.20
	−105	11.79	4.98
Potassium	0	12.4	4.7
	−33.2	11.86	4.95
	−50	12.3	5
	−100	12.2	4.82
	−33.5	12.05	4.87
Cesium	−50	25.1	2.34

Evaporation of their solutions in liquid ammonia results in the formation of metal-ammines having the formula $M(NH_3)_6$. Solutions of alkali and alkaline earth metals in liquid ammonia decrease in stability with increasing atomic weight of the metal; with time decomposition to hydrogen and metal amide occurs:

$$M + n\,NH_3 \rightarrow n/2\,H_2 + M(NH_2)_n$$

One of the most interesting properties of the dilute solutions of these metals in liquid ammonia is their characteristic deep blue color. This color is actually due to the short wavelength tail of a broad absorption band which possesses an absorption peak in the region of 7000 cm^{-1}. The spectra of all of the alkali metals are very

23

similar. In the region of the absorption peak, spectral measurements have not been made at concentrations greater than 0.01 M. However, observations have been carried out at the low frequency end of the band and alkali metal solutions have been shown to obey Beer's law up to concentrations as high as 0.2 M. It has been suggested that the absorption band at 7000 cm^{-1} represents an s $\rightarrow$ p electronic transition.

Solutions of sodium or potassium in liquid ammonia are paramagnetic. The molar magnetic susceptibility decreases with increasing metal concentration. When extrapolated to infinite dilution, the susceptibility approaches a value equal to that of a mole of free electrons. Thus, in very dilute solutions, the behavior approaches, but never quite achieves, that of a free electron gas for which the molar magnetic susceptibility $X_m = N\mu_0^2/kT$, where μ_0 is the magnetic moment of the electron. The measured susceptibilities increase with increase in temperature.

From studies of the paramagnetic resonance spectrum and the partial molar volumes, it has been calculated that in solutions of sodium in liquid ammonia the electron resides in a cavity having a radius of 3.0Å.

The electrical conductivities of these solutions are quite remarkable. They exceed those which have been observed for any other electrolytes in any known solvent. The equivalent conductances are from five to ten times greater than the values measured for aqueous solutions of highly ionized salts. The electron carriers conduct in much the same manner that they do in metals. The carrier of the negative charge is the same, irrespective of which alkali metal is dissolved.

In Figure 3–1, some data of Kraus (1921) have been plotted to show how the equivalent conductance changes with dilution. The equivalent conductance of a saturated solution of sodium in ammonia (not shown in the Figure) is almost seven times as large as that of free mercury metal. As the dilution is increased, the equivalent conductances fall and reach a minimum at concentrations of about 0.05 M. With further dilution the values increase abruptly and at infinite dilution (by extrapolation) reach values in excess of five times those obtained for ionic salts in water.

In order to interpret his results Kraus suggested that in the very dilute solutions, the alkali metals are dissociated to form solvated electrons and solvated cations

$$M + (n + x)\, NH_3 \rightleftarrows [M(NH_3)_n]^+ + e^-(NH_3)_x \qquad (1)$$

24

He attributed the fall in conductivity with increasing metal concentration and the minimum in the conductance *vs.* concentration plot to an association of the ionic species as ion pairs.

The magnetic susceptibility data which were reported subsequent to the investigations of Kraus revealed that a rapid decrease in molar susceptibility takes place at high concentrations of the metal. This required a modification of Kraus' model and an actual pairing mechanism was proposed

$$2 M^+ + 2 e^- \rightleftarrows M_2 \tag{2}$$

More recently Arnold and Patterson (1964), in order to satisfy the values of the equilibrium constants measured for equations (1) and (2), proposed the formation of another diamagnetic species, M^-,

$$M + e^- \rightleftarrows M^-$$

The most generally accepted model for alkali metal-ammonia solutions is one in which the solvated electron, in a cavity, retains its identity even while the other species are being formed. The species, M, may be viewed as an ion pair made of a solvated metal cation and a solvated electron held together by coulombic forces. The M^- and M_2 species may be described as ion quadrupoles made up of one or

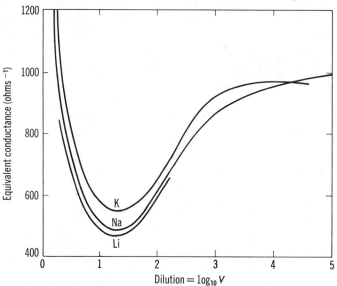

Figure 3–1 Equivalent conductance of alkali metals in liquid ammonia at $-33.5°$. V is the volume of liquid ammonia which dissolves one mole of metal. (From Kraus, ref. 6.)

two solvated metal ions and a pair of solvated electrons. In the moderately concentrated solutions, higher clusters such as M_3, etc., may exist. Finally, in very concentrated solutions, the solvated metal cations and electrons are bound together in a manner like that encountered in a fused metal.

3–D   SOME REACTIONS IN LIQUID AMMONIA

The nature of chemical reactions in liquid ammonia is easily understood when the similarity between the autoionization of ammonia and water is recognized. In terms of the Brönsted definition, the hydronium and the ammonium ions are the conjugate acids, and the hydroxide and the amide ions, the conjugate bases, of water and ammonia, respectively. The respective autoionizations are

$$2\,H_2O \rightleftarrows H_3O^+ + OH^-$$

and

$$2\,NH_3 \rightleftarrows NH_4^+ + NH_2^-$$

Neutralization, in the Brönsted sense, is defined as the reaction between an acid and a base to produce another acid and base; in the Arrhenius sense, it is the reaction between acid (proton) and base (hydroxide ion) to produce a salt and solvent (water); in the theory of solvent systems, it is defined as the reaction between the cation characteristic of the solvent and the anion characteristic of the solvent to produce solvent molecules; and finally, in the Lewis sense, it is represented as the reaction between an electron pair acceptor and an electron pair donor to produce a species containing a covalent bond between the two. The following reactions in liquid ammonia are readily understood in terms of each of these theories by consideration of the analogies with the water system.

In ammonia: $NH_4Cl + (Na^+)(:NH_2^-) \rightarrow (Na^+)(Cl^-) + 2\,NH_3$

In water: $HCl + (Na^+)(:OH^-) \rightarrow (Na^+)(Cl^-) + H_2O$

In ammonia: $6\,NH_4I + Mg_3N_2 \rightarrow 3\,[Mg^{+2}(2I^-)] + 8\,NH_3$

In water: $2\,HI + MgO \rightarrow (Mg^{+2})(2I^-) + H_2O$

Experimentally, neutralization reactions in liquid ammonia may be followed in the same manner as in water. For example, conductometric titrations can be performed in liquid NH_3 and the indicator, phenolphthalein, assumes an intense red color in basic solution, i.e.,

26

in the presence of alkali amides. Ammonium salt-amide titrations can be followed by the use of phenolphthalein as an indicator.

A further interesting analogy with the water system can be drawn in the precipitation from liquid ammonia of certain metallic amides, imides, or nitrides by the reaction of solutions of the metal salts with potassium amide. These reactions correspond to the precipitation of insoluble oxides and hydroxides in water as shown by the following examples.

In ammonia: $AgNO_3 + KNH_2 \rightarrow \underline{AgNH_2} + KNO_3$

In water: $2\,AgNO_3 + 2\,KOH \rightarrow \underline{Ag_2O} + 2\,KNO_3 + H_2O$

In ammonia: $Al^{+3} + 3\,NH_2^- \rightarrow \underline{Al(NH_2)_3}$

In water: $Al^{+3} + 3\,OH^- \rightarrow \underline{Al(OH)_3}$

In ammonia: $PbI_2 + 2\,KNH_2 \rightarrow \underline{PbNH} + 2\,KI + NH_3$

In water: $Pb(NO_3)_2 + 2\,KOH \rightarrow \underline{Pb(OH)_2} + 2\,KNO_3$

(1) Amphoteric Amides and Imides

A number of insoluble metallic amides exhibit amphoteric behavior in liquid ammonia in the sense that they dissolve in the presence of excess potassium amide by forming soluble amide complexes. Thus, when insoluble zinc amide is allowed to react with excess potassium amide in liquid ammonia, it dissolves as the complex tetraammono-zincate ion. The reactions involved are

$$Zn(NO_3)_2 + 2\,KNH_2 \rightarrow \underline{Zn(NH_2)_2} + 2\,KNO_3$$
$$\underline{Zn(NH_2)_2} + 2\,KNH_2 \rightleftarrows K_2[Zn(NH_2)_4]$$

Similarly, $Al(NH_2)_3$, $AgNH_2$ and $PbNH$, all of which are insoluble, dissolve in liquid ammonia as $[Al(NH_2)_4]^-$, $[Ag(NH_2)_2]^-$ and $[PbNH(NH_2)]^-$, respectively, when treated with excess potassium amide.

(2) Solvolytic Reactions

When antimony trichloride and phosphorus trichloride are added to water, they react rapidly with the solvent, in the one case to precipitate the basic salt, SbOCl, and in the other to form soluble phosphorous acid. Such reaction with the solvent (water) is termed *hydrolysis*. In an analogous manner, many compounds react with liquid ammonia to form new products.   Such reactions are termed *ammonolytic reactions*, and the process is known as *ammonolysis*. Typical examples of ammonolytic changes are

$$SiCl_4 \rightarrow Si(NH_2)_4 \xrightarrow{\Delta} Si_3N_4$$

$$TiCl_4 \rightarrow Ti(NH_2)_4 \xrightarrow{\Delta} Ti(NH)_2$$

$$GeCl_4 \rightarrow Ge(NH_2)_4 \xrightarrow{\Delta} Ge_3N_4$$

$$SnI_4 \xrightarrow{KNH_2} K_2[Sn(NH_2)_6]$$

$$PCl_5 \rightarrow P(NH_2)_5 \rightarrow P(NH)_2NH_2$$

$$PBr_3 \rightarrow P(NH_2)_3 \rightarrow P_2(NH)_3$$

$$MoCl_5 \rightarrow Mo(NH_2)_4Cl \text{ and other complexes.}$$

Many other ammonolytic reactions have been observed.

(3) Organic Reactions in Liquid Ammonia

A great deal of work has been done on reactions of organic and organometallic compounds in liquid ammonia, especially in metal-ammonia solutions.   This is much too extensive a subject to cover in detail.   Instead, a summary of the reactions between organic compounds and metal-ammonia solutions as they have been classified by Watt (1950) will be given.

1. When ammonolysis of the organic compound occurs and an ammonium salt is one of the products of the reaction, the equilibrium can be displaced completely in favor of formation of the organic product.   This is accomplished by removal of the ammonium ion by reaction with the metal solution.   The following two reactions are involved

$$RX + 2\,NH_3 \rightleftarrows RNH_2 + NH_4{}^+ + X^-$$

and

$$NH_4{}^+ + e^- \rightarrow NH_3 + 1/2\,H_2$$

2. Because of its basic character, ammonia has a great tendency to induce deprotonation of many organic compounds.   This permits the displacement of the active hydrogen by an alkali metal in compounds such as acetylene, triphenylmethane, alcohols, amines, acids, etc., with the formation of salts

$$RH + e^- \rightarrow R^- + 1/2\,H_2$$

28

The hydrogen which is formed may itself bring about further reduction or hydrogenation of the organic molecule. However, the electrons present in metal-ammonia solutions may also act as reducing agents.

3. There are cases where organometallics and compounds containing double or triple bonds are reduced by electrons, i.e., alkali metal solutions, to form anions which are converted to salts of the dissolved metal cations. Following are some examples

$$3 (C_6H_5)C\equiv CH + 4 Na + 2 NH_3 \rightarrow 2 (C_6H_5)C\equiv CNa$$
$$+ (C_6H_5)C_2H_5 + 2 NaNH_2$$
$$(CH_3)_3SnH + Na \rightarrow (CH_3)_3SnNa + 1/2 H_2$$
$$2 (CH_3)_3Ga \cdot NH_3 + 2 Na \rightarrow [(CH_3)_3Ga]_2Na_2 + 2 NH_3$$

4. The following bonds may be ruptured and the electrons may combine with each of the resulting fragments: C—C, Ge—Ge, Sn—Sn, C—Ge, C—Sn, Si—Ge, Si—Sn, C—O, Ge—O, Sn—O, C—N, Sn—N, S—S, C—S, Hg—C, and C—X.

5. Removal of halogen actually represents a case of C—X bond rupture and is classified separately because of the relative frequency of its occurrence. In this reaction, the halogen is always converted to the halide ion and the organic group may appear as a radical, it may undergo dimerization or ammonolysis, or it may be converted into the corresponding ion, as is exemplified by the following series of reactions.

$$RX + e^- \rightarrow R\cdot + X^-$$
$$R\cdot + R\cdot \rightarrow R—R$$
$$R^- + NH_3 \rightarrow RH + NH_2^-$$
$$RX + 2e^- \rightarrow R^- + X^-$$

6. In a few cases, metals in solution are able to remove oxygen atoms from an organic group. For example, nitro groups are reduced by sodium-ammonia solutions with the initial removal of an oxygen atom and formation of sodium oxide.

7. Solutions of alkali metals often demonstrate a catalytic effect, as in the polymerization of styrene.

3–E   THE UTILITY OF STUDIES IN LIQUID AMMONIA

One question frequently asked by students is: "What good is all this?"   This is a legitimate question, since, if practical ideas and useful materials were never to emerge from scientific research, funds for its support would certainly cease to exist, or would greatly diminish.   It is worthwhile to examine some results reported by Schechter and coworkers (1948) based on earlier work in the field. This research had practical commercial implications.

The superoxide ion, O_2^-, reacts with moisture according to the equation

$$2\,O_2^- + 2\,H_2O \rightarrow 2\,OH^- + H_2O_2 + O_2$$

The peroxide formed can be the source of additional molecular oxygen and the hydroxide is able to react irreversibly with carbon dioxide.   A superoxide is capable of fulfilling the dual purpose of acting as a carbon dioxide scavenger while at the same time serving as a source of molecular oxygen.   This would be ideal, for example, in a self-contained gas mask, i.e., one which does not selectively remove contaminating external gases but which does utilize water vapor of the exhaled breath to activate the superoxide.

Although potassium, rubidium and cesium were known to form superoxides, in 1948 sodium superoxide had not been characterized. From a strictly commercial viewpoint the sodium compounds are always the most important since they are the least expensive.

Schechter and coworkers investigated the reaction of molecular oxygen with solutions of sodium in liquid ammonia at $-77°C$.   The apparatus which they used is shown in Fig. 3–2.

It serves to illustrate some of the techniques employed in investigations of this type.   The sample of sodium metal was placed in a tared sampling stopcock G.   The sample was weighed and stored in a dry-box and was transferred, without exposure to the atmosphere, by means of the sample holder G.   After closing stopcock J, ammonia dried over sodium was introduced at A and condensed in the reaction cell F.   The latter was surrounded by a cooling bath E made up of equal volumes of carbon tetrachloride and chloroform to which Dry Ice was added.

When the desired amount of ammonia had been condensed, the sample of sodium, contained in G, was added by rotation of the stopcock.   Oxygen was introduced through the drying tube B containing

30

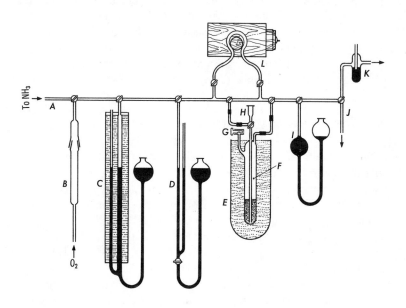

Figure 3–2 Apparatus for the study of the absorption of molecular oxygen by solutions of sodium in liquid ammonia. (From Schechter, Sisler, and Kleinberg, ref. 5.)

magnesium perchlorate until the gas buret C (surrounded by a water reservoir) was almost filled. The system was then closed by turning the stopcock above the drying tube. Oxygen was then pumped through the reaction cell and into reservoir I by the pump L. By proper manipulation of the stopcocks, the gas was returned to the buret and the cycle was repeated until there occurred no further change in the mercury level of the reservoir. The consumption of O_2 was a result of its reaction with the sodium dissolved in the liquid ammonia. The system was allowed to equilibrate, and the final static volume was determined.

The ammonia was then allowed to evaporate and to the solid in the reaction vessel was added, through H, a catalyst (an aqueous solution of $FeCl_3$ in HCl). The amount of gaseous oxygen liberated by the catalytic decomposition of the oxide was measured, and in this way the molar ratio of oxygen to sodium in the compound was determined.

These experiments revealed that about 50 percent of the metal had been converted to sodium superoxide. Although sodium superoxide has never been prepared commercially by the liquid ammonia process, this work established the existence of this useful compound and furnished the impetus for the subsequent research which resulted in a practical method for its manufacture.

3–F   HYDROCARBONS AS ACIDS AND BASES

Shatenshtein and coworkers have demonstrated experimentally that the hydrogen atoms of saturated hydrocarbons can be exchanged by deuterium and such behavior has been used as evidence of the acidity of these hydrocarbons. For example, exchange takes place when a mixture of a hydrocarbon and KND_2 (D is deuterium) in liquid ammonia is subjected to heating and stirring. The degree of deuterium exchange as a function of time is shown in Table 3–3, where C_1 is the concentration of D (atom %) initially present in the ammonia, C_2 is the corresponding value observed in the water of combustion obtained from the burning of the hydrocarbons after the experiment, and n is the average number of H atoms which have been replaced by D.

A similar experiment was performed by Y. G. Dubinskii. He used two separate isobutane preparations, one of which was labelled with deuterium in the methyl group and the other in the methine group (i.e., at the tertiary carbon atom). When heated at 120°C for

Table 3–3

Exchange of Hydrogen Atoms in Saturated Hydrocarbons at 120°

Hydrocarbon	$C_{KND_2}, N*$	Time (hours)	C_1	C_2	n
Isopentane	1.0	330	13.8	3.6	3.3
n-Heptane	1.0	500	95	17.6	3.0
Cetane (100°)	0.8	100	4.3	0.05	0.4
Ethylcyclobutane	1.0	510	14.3	4.9	4.1
Cyclopentane	3.0	1300	10.5	3.3	3.4
Cyclohexane	0.8	180	95	5.8	0.7
Decalin	0.8	180	95	3.5	1.0

* This is the concentration of KND_2 expressed as the normality.

32

100 hours in a 1 *N* potassium amide solution in ammonia, the methyl-labelled preparation showed 50% deuterium exchange while the other exhibited no exchange. This vividly demonstrated the greater acidity of the methyl hydrogens relative to those of the methine group. This strongly suggests that the mechanism of the exchange involves the formation of a carbanion rather than a carbonium ion.

Similar experiments, viz., hydrogen exchange with KND_2 in liquid ammonia, have been carried out with cyclopropane hydrocarbons. The cyclopropane hydrocarbons have been found to occupy a position between the paraffins and olefins with respect to rate of hydrogen atom exchange. It was found that ethylcyclopropane exchanges more rapidly than isopentane, but more slowly than vinylcyclopropane.

Among the unsaturated hydrocarbons, propene was found to exchange hydrogen much more rapidly than ethylene, with the order of exchange at the different positions in the propene molecule being $CH_3 > CH_2 > CH$. The most mobile hydrogen atoms in the olefin are those attached to the allylic position.

A number of olefins, viz., pentene-1 and -2, hexene-1, octene-1 and -2, 2-methyloctene-2 and tridecene-4 and -6, were found to undergo complete replacement of hydrogen by deuterium when dissolved in solutions of KND_2 in ND_3. Generally, with increase in the length of the carbon chain, a reduction in the average rate of exchange was observed.

The presence of unsaturation in an alicyclic molecule, whether the multiple bond is in the ring or in the side chain, ensures a complete exchange of the hydrogen atoms. In the case of dienes, only a very limited amount of information is available because of difficulties which arise from competing polymerization reactions.

Based upon the results just described, it seems well established that the H-atoms attached to unsaturated carbon atoms in dienes are much less mobile than the hydrogen atoms in —CH bonds in the allyl position.

3–G MECHANISM OF EXCHANGE AND ISOMERIZATION IN UNSATURATED HYDROCARBONS

It is generally agreed that the influence of a double bond does not extend over a long chain of carbon atoms. This conclusion is supported by results obtained under a variety of experimental conditions in which the isomerization of hydrocarbons is catalyzed by strong bases. It has been suggested (Gostunskaya, et al., 1956) that the first stage of the isomerization process involves the loss of a proton from the CH bond in the allyl position, where, as we have seen, the hydrogen atom is most labile. The isomerization equilibrium is described by

$$RCH_2\!-\!CH\!=\!CH_2 \underset{HA}{\overset{B}{\rightleftarrows}} [RCH\cdots CH\cdots CH_2]^- \underset{HA}{\overset{B}{\rightleftarrows}} RCH\!=\!CH\!-\!CH_3$$

In the above equation B is a base, e.g., potassium amide, and HA is an acid, and this acid can be a molecule of the hydrocarbon itself. The bracketed carbanion can be generated from either of the two isomers. The carbanion is not necessarily stable, but may represent an intermediate transition state.

That the carbanion is common to the two isomers has been determined by spectral studies of solutions in which potassium amide acts on either allyl- or propenylbenzene in liquid ammonia. In either case, the same spectrum is obtained (Rabinovitch, et al., 1962).

Experiments by Shatenshtein and coworkers suggest very strongly that an intimate relationship exists between the ease of hydrogen exchange and isomerization.

Liquid ammonia and liquid ammonia solutions containing potassium amide have been widely used to investigate hydrogen exchange in organic compounds. Other classes of compounds which have been studied in this manner include the aromatic hydrocarbons, ethers and amines. Alkali metal hydroxides and alkoxides have also been investigated as basic catalysts in this solvent. This general area of study represents one of the principal experimental techniques being used for the study of metallation, anionic polymerization and isomerization reactions.

From a preparative viewpoint, hydrogen exchange reactions in liquid ammonia have been found to be very useful in the preparation of deuterium- or tritium-labelled compounds. The more rapid exchange of *ortho*-hydrogens relative to *meta* and *para* hydrogens makes possible the synthesis of diphenyl ether-2,6,2′,6′-d$_4$.

This is accomplished by the action of a dilute solution of the deuterated amide on diphenyl ether.

Exercises

1. Write a reasonably detailed report on the preparation, purification and handling of one of the following solvents: hydrogen sulfide, phosgene, hydrazine, acetic acid, selenium oxychloride, bromine trifluoride.
2. From the original literature, cite specific examples which illustrate the seven categories of organic reactions which have been outlined in this chapter.
3. Give details of some experimental techniques which have been used in liquid ammonia for: (a) the study of visible and ultraviolet absorption spectra; (b) the determination of end points in neutralization reactions; (c) the measurement of electrode potentials.
4. Describe the conditions and write proper equations for the preparation of deuterium labelled compounds using ND_2^- and or ND_3.
5. Using standard textbooks and other literature references discuss (a) the reduction of inorganic compounds by alkali metal-ammonia solutions, and (b) the solubility of inorganic compounds in liquid ammonia.

References

1. W. L. Jolly and C. J. Hallada, Ch. 1 of *Nonaqueous Solvent Systems*, T. C. Waddington, Ed., Academic, 1965.
2. L. F. Audrieth and J. Kleinberg, Ch. 3–7 of *Nonaqueous Solvents*, Wiley, 1953.
3. G. W. Watt, *Chem. Revs.*, **46,** 289, 317 (1950).
4. A. I. Shatenshtein, Vol. I of *Advances in Physical Organic Chemistry*, V. Gold, Ed., Academic Press, 1962.
5. W. H. Schechter, H. H. Sisler and J. Kleinberg, *J. Am. Chem. Soc.*, **70,** 267 (1948).
6. C. A. Kraus, *ibid.*, **43,** 749 (1921).
7. W. L. Jolly, *Progress in Inorganic Chemistry*, Vol. I, F. A. Cotton, Ed., Interscience, 1959.
8. E. Arnold and A. Patterson, Jr., *Solutions Metal-Ammoniac*, G. Le Poutre and M. Sienko, Eds., W. A. Benjamin, 1964.
9. G. E. Coates, *Organo-metallic Compounds*, Wiley, 1960.
10. I. V. Gostunskaya, N. I. Tyun'kina, and B. A. Kazanskii, *Doklady Akad. Nauk S.S.S.R.*, **108,** 473 (1956).
11. E. A. Rabinovich, I. V. Astaf'ev, and A. I. Shatenshtein, *Zhur. Obshchei Khim.*, **32,** 748, (1962).

CHAPTER 4

Anhydrous Hydrogen Fluoride

4-A GENERAL CONSIDERATIONS

In spite of the fact that it is highly corrosive and physiologically hazardous, liquid hydrogen fluoride has ceased to be a laboratory curiosity and is now firmly established in the chemical industry. Interest in this solvent, in both the industrial and academic environments, continues to grow. Many useful chemical products have already emerged from research with this solvent, and many more may be expected.

Liquid hydrogen fluoride bears a remarkable resemblance to water (Table 3-1). Since it freezes at $-83°C$ and boils at $19.5°C$, it presents the investigator with the opportunity for study in a liquid phase which exists over a temperature range even greater than that of water. It is a very highly associated liquid, due to the F—H---F hydrogen bond which is one of the strongest known. The enthalpy of the F—H---F bond in gaseous hydrogen fluoride has been estimated to be between 6.7 and 7.0 kcal/mole. By comparison, the enthalpy of the O—H---O bond in water vapor has been estimated to be between 4.4 and 5.0 kcal/mole, and that of the N—H---N bond in ammonia between 3.7 and 4.4 kcal/mole. Hydrogen fluoride possesses outstanding solvent properties, but analogies between it and the water system are restricted because of the ease with which solvolysis occurs in this solvent.

The preparation of pure anhydrous hydrogen fluoride, although not difficult, requires care. This substance possesses a voracious appetite for water and the removal of the last traces of water from potassium hydrogen fluoride, KHF_2, from which the anhydrous solvent is prepared, is accomplished by electrolysis in an inert vessel constructed either of copper or stainless steel. Hydrogen fluoride is then obtained by decomposing the fused potassium acid fluoride thermally between 500 and 600°. The pure hydrogen fluoride generated during this process is then condensed in an appropriate vessel. A commercial grade of hydrogen fluoride containing small amounts of water, silicon tetrafluoride, and sulfur dioxide as impurities can be prepared by the reaction between commercial fluorspar (mainly CaF_2) and concentrated sulfuric acid. Because the interest in this solvent has increased so much, containers, tubing, and vessels of chemically resistant materials for handling it are now commercially available. Particularly noteworthy are the fluorine-containing plastics such as polytetrafluoroethylene and polychlorotrifluoroethylene which are completely inert to hydrogen fluoride.

4–B   SOLVENT PROPERTIES OF HYDROGEN FLUORIDE TOWARD INORGANIC SUBSTANCES

The simple dissolution of solutes in liquid hydrogen fluoride is a most infrequent occurrence. In the majority of cases solvolysis occurs with the fluoride ion being one of the end products. Very few salts dissociate in this solvent into their simple ions.

The introduction of water into the solvent leads to a very vigorous reaction. With excess hydrogen fluoride, water forms the hydronium ion and hydrogen fluoride ion according to the equilibrium

$$H_2O + 2\,HF \rightleftarrows H_3O^+ + HF_2^-$$

A number of different crystalline solvates have been identified, among which are $H_2O \cdot HF$, $H_2O \cdot 2\,HF$, $H_2O \cdot 4\,HF$.

We are familiar with the fact that oxides and hydroxides of metals will dissolve easily in aqueous solutions of mineral acids. It is not surprising, therefore, to find that these same substances react violently with the formation of water and the metal fluorides when introduced into liquid hydrogen fluoride. The alkali metals, which react vigorously with water, do likewise when introduced into anhydrous hydrogen fluoride. The resistance of the noble metals to chemical attack by liquid hydrogen fluoride makes vessels and other apparatus constructed of these materials useful when working with this solvent.

The fluorides of the alkali metals, as well as ammonium fluoride, and, to a somewhat lesser degree the fluorides of the alkaline earth metals, silver and thallous fluoride, are soluble in liquid hydrogen fluoride. It is probable that in the case of these fluorides, solution is accompanied by solvate formation. For example, the following addition compounds have been isolated and identified: $KF \cdot HF$, $KF \cdot 2\,HF$, $KF \cdot 3\,HF$ and $NH_4F \cdot 5\,HF$. It is generally believed that in solutions of metal fluorides the HF_2^- anion is present. This anion possesses an exceedingly stable hydrogen bond.

It has been found by Jache and Cady (1952) that the fluorides, in their solubilities, behave very much like the corresponding hydroxides in water. Jache and Cady observed that the fluorides of the alkali and alkaline earth elements are soluble, and that their solubility increases as one goes to elements of higher atomic weight in the respective families. Strontium fluoride is out of line, but its high solubility as compared to that of barium fluoride is probably due to the difference in degree of solvation of the solid phases of the two substances. Jache and Cady suggest that what are being compared here are the solubilities of $SrF_2 \cdot 3\,HF$ and $BaF_2 \cdot 6\,HF$. Probably $BaF_2 \cdot 3\,HF$, if it could exist in liquid hydrogen fluoride, would be more soluble than $SrF_2 \cdot 3\,HF$. The fluorides of zinc, cadmium, and mercury are less soluble than the alkaline earth fluorides. There is a decrease in solubility in the order: sodium fluoride, magnesium fluoride, aluminum fluoride. The expected type of behavior is shown by silver, mercury, thallium, and iron in that the lower valent fluorides are more soluble than those in which the metal has its higher valence. By contrast, the higher valent fluorides of cerium and cobalt (CeF_4 and CoF_3) are the more soluble.

Several of the fluorides, particularly silver(I) fluoride, are relatively more soluble than the corresponding hydroxides are in water and none is strikingly less soluble. Perhaps this means that on the whole, fluorides are more basic in hydrogen fluoride than the hydroxides are in water.

A few salts, other than fluorides, including the nitrates of sodium and silver, the sulfates of sodium and potassium, as well as the alkali chlorates, bromates, iodates, perchlorates, and periodates, dissolve to form fairly stable solutions.

The solvolytic reactions which accompany the introduction of many solutes into liquid HF are predictable. In terms of simple equilibria, for example, alkali metal halides other than the fluorides dissolve with the evolution of the respective gaseous hydrogen halides because of the insolubility of the gaseous hydrogen halides in the solvent. Similarly, potassium cyanide dissolves with the evolution of hydrogen cyanide. Just as carbonates react with aqueous mineral acids, to yield gaseous carbon dioxide, calcium, zinc, and lead carbonates decompose with the evolution of carbon dioxide on contact with liquid HF.

4–C SOLUBILITY OF ORGANIC COMPOUNDS IN HYDROGEN FLUORIDE

Organic compounds, as a group, are either very soluble or almost insoluble in this solvent. Saturated aliphatic hydrocarbons are insoluble, while unsubstituted aromatics are only slightly soluble. The solubility of substituted aromatics depends almost entirely upon the nature of the substituent groups. Both aromatic and aliphatic derivatives are soluble in hydrogen fluoride if there are present N, S, or O atoms or unsaturated groups which can act as basic centers. When an organic compound is very soluble, this solubility is invariably accompanied by a reaction with the solvent. It can be stated that as the acidity of the organic molecule increases, its solubility in hydrogen fluoride decreases.

Alcohols, aldehydes, ketones, ethers, acids, acid anhydrides, and a number of nitrogen derivatives give conducting solutions in this solvent. The conducting ions are complex cations (onium ions) formed by the reaction of the organic molecule with the solvent. The following are typical reactions:

$$CH_3OH + HF \rightarrow (CH_3OH \cdot H)^+ + F^-$$
$$CH_3CO_2H + HF \rightarrow (CH_3CO_2H \cdot H)^+ + F^-$$
$$(C_2H_5)_2O + HF \rightarrow [(C_2H_5)_2O \cdot H]^+ + F^-$$

These ionization reactions take place because of the extreme acidity of hydrogen fluoride. All of the reacting substances behave as bases in this solvent.

4–D INORGANIC REACTIONS INVOLVING ACID-BASE RELATIONSHIPS

It has already been pointed out that anhydrous hydrogen fluoride is a solvent of high dielectric constant and that the dipole moment of this molecule is actually larger than that of water. It is, therefore, not surprising that autoionization occurs to a considerable extent as indicated by

$$2\,HF \rightleftharpoons H_2F^+ + F^-$$

This equation must be considered strictly an approximation. The proton is probably associated to hydrogen fluoride polymers rather than to a monomeric hydrogen fluoride molecule. Also, because of the great stability of the hydrogen bond in the HF_2^- ion, the fluoride ion must be strongly solvated. The extent to which autoionization occurs in pure liquid hydrogen fluoride has not been firmly established.

The number of substances which behave as acids in hydrogen fluoride is greatly limited because of the extreme acidity of the solvent. In order for a substance to behave as an acid in this solvent, it must be able to remove the fluoride ion from the hydrogen fluoride molecule to produce the acid species, H_2F^+. Those substances which are capable of behaving as acids in this medium are limited almost entirely to derivatives of hydrogen fluoride. These include antimony(V) fluoride and boron trifluoride, which, upon dissolution in this medium, give rise to SbF_6^- and BF_4^-, i.e., to the acids $H(SbF_6)$ and $H(BF_4)$. Similarly, $H(AsF_6)$ and $H(PF_6)$ also behave as acids in this solvent. Solutions of these acids in liquid hydrogen fluoride vigorously attack many metals.

It is of interest to note that cryolite, Na_3AlF_6, is quite soluble in anhydrous hydrogen fluoride and that upon addition of fluoroboric acid to a solution of cryolite in the solvent precipitation of aluminum fluoride takes place. This reaction is analogous to the precipitation of aluminum hydroxide from solutions of sodium aluminate in water as shown by

$$Na_3(AlF_6) + 3\,H(BF_4) \rightarrow \underline{AlF_3} + 3\,Na(BF_4) + 3\,HF$$

and in water

$$NaAl(OH)_4 + H_3O^+ \rightarrow \underline{Al(OH)_3} + Na^+ + 2\,H_2O$$

Chromium(III) fluoride is insoluble in hydrogen fluoride. However, together with sodium fluoride, chromic fluoride dissolves according to the equation

$$CrF_3 + 3\,NaF \rightarrow Na_3CrF_6$$

The addition of fluoroboric acid to this solution causes the chromic fluoride to be reprecipitated

$$Na_3CrF_6 + 3\,H(BF_4) \rightarrow 3\,Na(BF_4) + \underline{CrF_3} + 3\,HF$$

4–E ORGANIC REACTIONS IN LIQUID HYDROGEN FLUORIDE

It appears to be well established that so far as practical applications are concerned, liquid hydrogen fluoride will continue to have its most significant impact in the field of organic chemistry.

We are well aware of the difficulties involved in handling elementary fluorine. As a chemical, elementary fluorine is well known for its outstanding ability to oxidize almost all other substances. Liquid hydrogen fluoride is unique in being itself inert toward elementary fluorine. Hence, it is in a class by itself as a medium in which to carry out fluorination reactions. Such reactions must be carried out in the completely anhydrous solvent, and the presence of a catalyst, such as a heavy metal halide, or antimony metal or iodine, is necessary. A large number of organic compounds has been successfully fluorinated in this medium. These include hydrocarbons, ethers, and many types of substituted derivatives.

Aromatic fluorides can be obtained by carrying out the classical diazotization reaction in anhydrous HF. The reaction sequence is indicated by

$$ArNH_2 \xrightarrow[\text{HF}]{\text{NaNO}_2} ArN_2F \to ArF + N_2$$

Diazotization in HF is especially useful because it has made possible the preparation of ortho-substituted fluorine derivatives directly from the ortho-substituted amines.

Among other types of organic reactions which have been performed successfully in this solvent are nitration and sulfonation and several well known molecular rearrangements, such as the Beckman and Fries rearrangements. Without question, however, the most successful reactions have been those in which fluorine-containing compounds have been obtained by electrochemical methods.

4–F ELECTROLYSIS OF ORGANIC COMPOUNDS IN ANHYDROUS HYDROGEN FLUORIDE

The success of the electrochemical fluorination processes results from the fact that conducting organic species are formed upon dissolution of a wide variety of organic compounds in liquid hydrogen fluoride. Electrolysis reactions are normally carried out in a steel cell containing nickel electrodes; fluorination of the dissolved substance occurs at the anode while hydrogen is evolved at the cathode.

41

Relatively low voltages, about 6 volts, are used to avoid production of both hydrogen and fluorine which would occur at higher voltages. This highly effective fluorination method has resulted in commercial preparation of a number of highly useful fluoro derivatives, e.g., trifluoroacetic acid, perfluorocarbons, perfluorosulphonyl fluorides, etc. The importance of organic fluorine containing compounds, such as the fluorinated refrigerating gases and the chemically inert plastic materials, is well known. Because of the established importance and the great potential of the electrolytic process for the preparation of organic fluoro derivatives, let us examine this method in somewhat greater detail. The electrolytic cells are constructed of iron or nickel. The anodes are of nickel while the cathodes are of nickel or steel. Provision must be made for condensation of the volatile hydrogen fluoride, as well as for the removal of the fluorinated products. The basic design of such an electrolytic apparatus is shown in Figure 4–1.

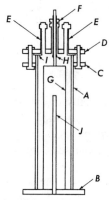

Figure 4–1 Typical cell for electrolytic fluorination.   *A*, cell body (of iron); *B*, iron base plate; *C*, flange; *D*, lid; *E*, inlet and outlet tubes; *F*, anode support; *G*, anode; *H*, polyvinyl chloride insulation; *I*, polyvinyl chloride gasket; *J*, central cathode.

Organic compounds which contain oxygen, nitrogen, or sulfur give conducting solutions in liquid HF through the formation of onium salts (p. 39). When the organic compounds are soluble, but form nonconducting species, an inorganic salt such as lithium or potassium fluoride must be added to impart sufficient electrical conductivity to the solution. The electrolysis is usually carried out at a current density of about 0.02 amps/cm^2 at a potential of 5–6 volts.

The electrochemical fluorination procedure as developed by J. H. Simons has achieved remarkable success, especially in the preparation of compounds in which all hydrogen atoms are replaced by fluorine atoms, the perfluoro derivatives. The most significant results have been achieved with those organic compounds which do form conducting solutions when dissolved in anhydrous hydrogen fluoride, namely nitrogen-, oxygen-, and sulfur-containing compounds. The following equation illustrates the preparation of perfluoromethyl amine from dry trimethyl amine

$$(CH_3)_3N \xrightarrow[\text{4-8V, 2 amp-dm}^2]{\text{HF}} (CF_3)_3N + CHF_3 + CF_4 + NF_3$$

Other examples of important electrochemical reactions carried out in this solvent are found in the electrolysis of carboxylic acids and of their anhydrides (or chlorides). Acetic anhydride yields perfluoroacetyl fluoride

$$(CH_3CO)_2O \xrightarrow[\text{5.2V, 50 amps}]{\text{HF}} CF_3COF$$

The electrolysis of methanesulfonyl chloride, CH_3SO_2Cl, gives trifluoromethanesulfonyl fluoride, CF_3SO_2F. The electrolytic fluorination process, as it has been applied to the alkanesulfohalides to form the corresponding perfluoroalkanesulfofluorides, has been studied in great detail by R. N. Haszeldine in England.

Among other electrochemical processes that have been carried out are the addition of fluorine across double bonds, the replacement of specific hydrogen atoms by fluorine in aliphatic acids, and the fluorination of carbon disulfide, but these reactions have not yet achieved commercial importance.

4–G PREPARATION OF THE FREONS

The fluorinated halogen derivatives of methane and ethane represent a most important group of refrigerating gases and are also widely used as pressurizing agents. The term "freons" has been applied to this group of compounds. This is the commercial name adopted by the DuPont Company. However, a number of other American and European firms manufacture identical compounds.

At the present time these important chemicals are manufactured on a continuous basis from carbon tetrachloride dissolved in anhydrous hydrogen fluoride with antimony salts acting as "transfer catalysts." The "transfer catalysts" are prepared by the dissolution of antimony pentachloride in hydrogen fluoride. The chemistry of this process can be expressed in its simplest form by the following sequence of equations:

$$SbCl_5 + n\ HF \longrightarrow SbF_nCl_{(5-n)} + n\ HCl$$

$$CCl_4 + HF \xrightarrow{R*} CCl_3F + HCl$$

$$CCl_3F + HF \xrightarrow{R*} CCl_2F_2 + HCl$$

$$CCl_2F_2 + HF \xrightarrow{R*} CClF_3 + HCl$$

The actual reactions are much more complicated than is indicated by this reaction sequence. A mixture of freons is obtained, but their separation is not difficult since their boiling points differ considerably. It is of interest to note that the antimony must be in the pentavalent form to function as a catalyst. Fluorinated ethane derivatives are prepared in the same manner from hexachloroethane.

4-H   ADDITION OF HYDROGEN FLUORIDE TO UNSATURATED BONDS

When unsaturated hydrocarbons react with gaseous hydrogen fluoride, polymerization to high molecular weight compounds often takes place. However, at low temperatures, i.e., in anhydrous liquid hydrogen fluoride, addition across the unsaturated bond occurs. For example, propylene is converted to 2-fluoropropane and cyclohexene to fluorocyclohexane in yields of 61 and 70%, respectively. In the case of the dienes, the addition of hydrogen fluoride must be carried out at very low temperatures to avoid polymerization. Propadiene adds two moles of hydrogen fluoride at $-70°$ to form 2,2-difluoropropane. The addition of hydrogen fluoride to substituted acetylenes, $HC\equiv CR$, is accomplished in yields of 85–90% by the introduction of the acetylene into liquid hydrogen fluoride containing oxygenated molecules such as ether or acetone. Both fluorine atoms add to the carbon atom which was originally proton bare.

---

* $R = SbF_nCl_{(5-n)}$

44

Exercises

1. Present either an oral or a written report on the Balz-Schiemann reaction.
2. How is hydrogen fluoride manufactured commercially?
3. Present either an oral or a written report on the nature of the electrical conductivity of solutions of alcohols, nitrobenzene, potassium fluoride, and sodium fluoride in anhydrous hydrogen fluoride.
4. Discuss the structure of liquid hydrogen fluoride based upon evidence obtained from density, proton nuclear magnetic resonance, electrical conductivity, infrared, and other physical measurements.
5. Using the references cited at the end of this chapter, investigate the manner in which HF adds to an acetylenic compound in which both carbon atoms are proton bare, e.g., $CH_3C{\equiv}CCH_3$.

References

1. A. W. Jache and G. H. Cady, *J. Phys. Chem.*, **56**, 1106 (1952).
2. H. H. Hyman and J. J. Katz, Ch. 2 of *Nonaqueous Solvent Systems*, T. C. Waddington, Ed., Academic, 1965.
3. M. Hudlicky, *Chemistry of Organic Fluorine Compounds*, Macmillan, 1962.
4. J. H. Simons, *Fluorine Chemistry*, Vol. I–V, Academic Press, 1950–1964.
5. T. Gramstad and R. N. Haszeldine, *J. Chem. Soc.*, 173 (1956); 2640 (1957); 4069 (1957).
6. J. Burdon and J. C. Tatlow, "The Electrochemical Process for the Synthesis of Fluoro-organic Compounds," in *Advances in Fluorine Chemistry*, M. Stacey, J. C. Tatlow, and A. G. Sharpe, Eds., Butterworths, 1960.

5–A   GENERAL CONSIDERATIONS

Thus far our discussion of nonaqueous solvents has been confined to the protonic solvents, ammonia and hydrogen fluoride. Let us turn now to what has become the most widely studied nonprotonic solvent, liquid sulfur dioxide. This solvent exists as a liquid over the temperature range $-75.6°$ to $-10.1°C$. The physical constants for this solvent are given in Table 5-1.

Chemically, sulfur dioxide is not nearly as reactive as hydrogen fluoride, nor does it require as low a temperature for study as does liquid ammonia. Therefore, from the manipulative point of view, it is easier to handle than the previously discussed protonic solvents. Its availability, preparation and purification do not require involved processes. Its dielectric constant, which is 15.4 at 0.2°C, is considerably smaller than that of either hydrogen fluoride or water. Therefore, as an ionizing solvent, it is much less effective than either of the latter solvents. Its dielectric constant, however, is large enough that it does dissolve a number of salts. It is a much better solvent for covalent than for ionic compounds.

Liquid sulfur dioxide has found important applications as a solvent in petroleum refining. It was widely used as a refrigerant, but it has been replaced by the freons for this purpose.

46

Table 5–1

Some Physical Constants of Sulfur Dioxide

Property	Value	Temperature (°C)
Melting point	−75.6°C	—
Boiling point	−10.1°C	—
Liquid range	65°	
Enthalpy of fusion (kcal/mole)	1.9691	−75.6
Enthalpy of vaporization (kcal/mole)	5.96	−10.1
Vapor pressure (cm Hg)	28.48	−30
	53.06	−20
	115.96	0
	171.4	10
	2456.0	20
Viscosity of liquid	$\eta = 4.03 - 0.0363T(°C)$	
Dielectric constant of liquid	15.4	0.2
Dipole moment (Debyes)	1.62	16.3
S—O Bond length (Å)	1.43	—
O—S—O Bond angle	119.5°	
Density (g cm^{-3})	1.46	−10.1
Specific conductivity (ohm^{-1}cm^{-1})	$3 - 4 \times 10^{-8}$	−10
Molar ebullioscopic constant (deg/mole)	1.48	
Molar cryoscopic constant (deg/mole)	0.0393	

It is readily available and is low in cost and easily purified. The impurities in commercial tank sulfur dioxide are traces of water and sulfur trioxide. These are readily removed by bringing the gas first into contact with sulfuric acid and then with phosphorus pentoxide. The liquid is condensed and used in a closed system so that contact with atmospheric moisture is avoided. Pure sulfur dioxide can be prepared at the laboratory bench by the reaction of sulfuric acid with a quality grade sulfite, usually sodium sulfite. Sulfur dioxide is an extremely toxic material and it must be handled with great care.

5–B   SOLUBILITY OF INORGANIC SUBSTANCES

Covalent compounds as a group are more soluble in liquid sulfur dioxide than are ionic compounds because of its low dielectric constant. The latter require a solvent of high dielectric constant and high solvation energy to overcome the strong crystalline forces which bind the ions together. The halogens and covalent inorganic compounds such as the interhalogens, boron halides, the group VA halides and oxyhalides, the group IV tetrahalides and the thionyl compounds are either completely miscible with this solvent or very soluble therein.

Among inorganic salts, the iodides and thiocyanates of the alkali metals are quite soluble. The solubilities of the halides of a given alkali metal decrease as the size of the halide ion decreases. The ammonium halides display a solubility pattern which parallels that of the alkali metal halides, but which is much more striking. The solubilities of various ammonium salts per thousand grams of SO_2 at 0° are : NH_4Cl, 1.67 g; NH_4Br, 6.0 g; NH_4I, 580 g; NH_4SCN, 6160 g.

Other moderately soluble salts are the sulfites, cyanides, and acetates of the alkali metals. Oxides and hydroxides are insoluble whereas nitrates react with the solvent so that their equilibrium solubilities are not experimentally determinable.

A number of stable solvates have been isolated and, as is to be expected, most of the stable solvates are formed with those salts which are appreciably soluble. Some examples of the solvates which have been isolated are $NaI·4 SO_2$, $NaI·2 SO_2$, $SrI_2·2 SO_2$, $KSCN·SO_2$, $AlCl_3·SO_2$ and $KSCN·\frac{1}{2} SO_2$. It has been pointed out by Jander, one of the pioneers in liquid sulfur dioxide research, that solvate formation does not occur solely with the readily soluble salts. Other factors which affect solvate formation are the temperature coefficient of solubility and the lattice energy of the solvate. With few exceptions, however, solvate formation is confined to the alkali and alkaline earth metal and ammonium or substituted ammonium salts with iodide, thiocyanate, bromide, chloride, or fatty acid radicals as anions.

5–C   SOLUBILITY OF ORGANIC COMPOUNDS

With the exception of the saturated aliphatic compounds, which possess only limited solubility, liquid sulfur dioxide serves as an excellent general solvent for organic compounds. Organic substances containing almost any functional group are readily soluble. The marked difference in solubility which exists between the saturated aliphatic and aromatic hydrocarbons has had some important industrial applications.

Although natural petroleum contains a wide variety of substances and complicated solubility relations exist, useful separations can frequently be obtained. For instance, diesel fuel must contain a very low percentage of aromatic hydrocarbons. When kerosene is extracted with SO_2 at $-10°$ most of the aromatics can be removed and paraffin-rich fuel, very suitable for diesel applications, can be obtained.

5–D ACID-BASE REACTIONS IN LIQUID SULFUR DIOXIDE

The exact nature of the autoionization of liquid sulfur dioxide is not well understood and the following dissociation scheme is *not accurate*, but it is useful

$$2 SO_2 \rightleftarrows SO^{+2} + SO_3^{-2} \tag{1}$$

Reasoning according to the theory of solvent systems, thionyl compounds, e.g., $SOCl_2$, should behave as acids in liquid sulfur dioxide, while sulfites should be bases in this solvent. A neutralization reaction, viz., the reaction between an acid and a base to yield the parent solvent and salt, would involve the reaction between the thionyl ion and the sulfite ion to form sulfur dioxide. It is possible, using a conductimetric titration technique, to follow a neutralization reaction in this solvent.

The conductimetric titration of tetramethylammonium sulfite by thionyl chloride in liquid sulfur dioxide is particularly interesting. The course of this reaction as reported by Jander is shown in Figure 5–1. There is an experimental break at a point corresponding approximately to the addition half-mole of sulfite per mole of thionyl chloride. It has been postulated that this break corresponds to the formation of an acid salt, but this interpretation is currently in doubt. A second sharp break close to the 1:1 equivalence point is easily observed.

Amphoteric behavior in liquid sulfur dioxide has been demonstrated by the reaction between aluminum chloride and tetramethylammonium sulfite. A precipitate of aluminum sulfite is initially

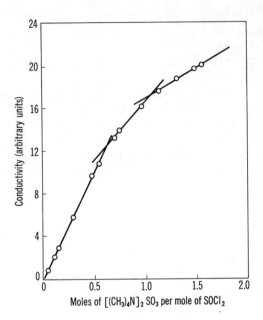

Figure 5-1 Conductimetric titration of $SOCl_2$ against $[(CH_3)_4N]_2SO_3$. Jander and Immig, *Z. anorg. Chem.*, **233**, 295 (1937).]

formed, the reaction shown by the equation

$$2 AlCl_3 + 3 [(CH_3)_4N]_2SO_3 \rightarrow \underline{Al_2(SO_3)_3} + 6 (CH_3)_4NCl$$

taking place. Further addition of tetramethylammonium sulfite dissolves the precipitate with the formation of a sulfito complex of aluminum

$$Al_2(SO_3)_3 + 3 [(CH_3)_4N]_2SO_3 \rightleftarrows 2 [(CH_3)_4N]_3[Al(SO_3)_3]$$

Addition of the acid, thionyl chloride, reprecipitates aluminum sulfite

$$2 [(CH_3)_4N]_3[Al(SO_3)_3] + 3 SOCl_2 \rightarrow$$
$$\underline{Al_2(SO_3)_3} + 6 [N(CH_3)_4]Cl + 6 SO_2$$

5-E   METATHETICAL REACTIONS IN LIQUID SULFUR DIOXIDE

A sequence of reactions in which the halide salts are precipitated quantitatively in every case, illustrates the formation of thionyl derivatives

$$2\,NH_4SCN + SOCl_2 \rightarrow SO(SCN)_2 + \underline{2\,NH_4Cl}$$
$$2\,Ag(CH_3CO_2) + SOCl_2 \rightarrow SO(CH_3CO_2)_2 + \underline{2\,AgCl}$$
$$2\,KBr + SOCl_2 \rightarrow SOBr_2 + \underline{2\,KCl}$$

It should be pointed out that only thionyl bromide was isolated in the pure state from the reactions described above. The addition of thionyl chloride to potassium iodide in this solvent yields a precipitate of potassium chloride, but thionyl iodide is not formed. Instead, elementary iodine and sulfur are observed to form, probably according to the reaction sequence

$$2\,SOI_2 \rightarrow 2\,I_2 + 2\,SO$$
$$2\,SO \rightarrow SO_2 + S$$

5–F COMPLEX COMPOUND FORMATION

Some of the complexation reactions which are familiar to us in the aqueous system occur also in liquid sulfur dioxide. For instance, iron(III) forms the characteristic red thiocyanate complex, and molecular iodine increases the conductivity of alkali metal iodides. This increased conductivity can be interpreted in terms of the formation of the well known triiodide ion. Another typical example is the apparent formation of the complex iodides of Cd(II) and Hg(II), since the solubility of the iodides of these elements is greatly increased by the addition of alkali iodide.

The oxidation of potassium iodide by antimony pentachloride has been studied quantitatively. This reaction involves an oxidation-reduction reaction as well as complex formation. The stoichiometry of the overall reaction is given as follows:

$$6\,KI + 3\,SbCl_5 \rightarrow 2\,K_3(SbCl_6) + SbCl_3 + 3\,I_2$$
$$2\,K_3(SbCl_6) + 6\,SbCl_5 \rightarrow 6\,K(SbCl_6) + 2\,SbCl_3$$

The conductimetric titration of antimony(III) chloride with thionyl chloride shows a very well-defined break at the ratio of two moles of antimony compound to three moles of thionyl compound. These data have been interpreted in terms of the existence of a complex $(SO)_3(SbCl_6)_2$. An interesting reaction occurs when antimony(V) chloride in sulfur dioxide is treated with nitrosyl chloride. The pure, bright yellow compound, $(NO)(SbCl_6)$ is obtained. Other derivatives of the hexachloroantimonate(V) ion are shown in the following equations which represent reactions carried out in liquid sulfur dioxide

$$(CH_3CO)(SbCl_6) + KCl \rightarrow CH_3COCl + K(SbCl_6)$$
$$(CH_3CO)(SbCl_6) + NOCl \rightarrow CH_3COCl + (NO)(SbCl_6)$$
$$(NO)(SbCl_6) + [(CH_3)_4N]ClO_4 \rightarrow [(CH_3)_4N](SbCl_6) + \underline{(NO)(ClO_4)}$$

5–G TRACER STUDIES IN LIQUID SULFUR DIOXIDE

Jander (1949) proposed the following ionization scheme for liquid sulfur dioxide

$$3\,SO_2 \rightleftarrows SO^{+2} + S_2O_5^{-2}$$

and suggested that thionyl chloride ionizes in the solvent in a manner described by the equilibrium

$$SOCl_2 \rightleftarrows SO^{+2} + 2\,Cl^-$$

It was pointed out by Bateman, Hughes, and Ingold (1944) that although the interpretation according to the solvent system theory is consistent with many of the chemical reactions observed in liquid sulfur dioxide, *it is not a necessary consequence.* They suggested that the ionization of thionyl chloride in sulfur dioxide was very likely

$$SOCl_2 \rightleftarrows SOCl^+ + Cl^-$$

The use of radioactive tracers has furnished a most useful tool for testing the validity of these concepts. This subject has been discussed in a review by Norris (1959).

When thionyl bromide or chloride tagged with the radioactive isotope ^{35}S was added to tracer-free liquid SO_2, it was found that ^{35}S exchange was negligibly slow, i.e., radioactivity was not detected in the solvent. These results cast considerable doubt on the validity of the Jander ionization schemes. If the solvent and the thionyl compounds both ionized to give SO^{+2} ions, the exchange should have been instantaneous since this ion is common to both equilibria.

Additional experiments involved the use of pyrosulfite $(S_2O_5^{-2})$ which is known to give sulfite ions in sulfur dioxide solution. When

52

pyrosulfite tagged with ^{35}S was added to liquid sulfur dioxide as the tetramethylammonium salt ($NMe_4[O_2S{-}SO_3]$), exchange of the radioactive species with the solvent was complete within 20 minutes, even at Dry-Ice temperatures. The investigators (Johnson, *et al.*, 1951) postulated a *nonionic, direct oxide transfer mechanism* for the exchange:

$$^{35}SO_3^{-2} + SO_2 \rightleftarrows SO_3^{-2} + {}^{35}SO_2$$

Such a mechanism by-passes completely any ionization step. It presents a situation analogous to that of exchange of oxygen between hydronium ions and water which involves proton exchange without intermediate self-ionization of the water

$$H_3O^+ + H_2{}^{18}O \rightleftarrows H_2O + H_3{}^{18}O^+$$

This proposal implies that acid-base chemistry in the solvent sulfur dioxide involves oxide ions possessing a remarkable mobility, about equal in fact, to the mobility of protons in aqueous solutions. Nakata (1943), using ^{18}O as a tracer, observed a rapid exchange between sulfur dioxide and sulfur trioxide in the liquid phase, whereas Huston (1951) using ^{35}S found the rate of exchange between SO_2 and SO_3 to be negligibly slow. These results confirm that the exchange reaction must be either

$$SO_2 + SO_3 \rightleftarrows SO^{+2} + SO_4^{-2}$$

or that it must proceed through an intermediate of the type

in which the sulfur atoms remain nonequivalent. It appears, therefore, that a strong case has been made for a mobile oxide ion mechanism. As we shall now see, this is not the whole story.

The thionyl halide-sulfur dioxide ^{35}S exchange has been shown to be negligibly slow as was pointed out in the first part of this discussion. When a Lewis base, in the form of a soluble bromide or chloride, e.g., as a quaternary ammonium or alkali halide, is added to a solution of $SOCl_2$ or $SOBr_2$ in liquid SO_2, ^{35}S exchange becomes quite rapid, i.e., it is "base-catalyzed." The interpretation of the kinetic data obtained from such base-catalyzed systems requires that the halide ions possess a rapid mobility. This indicates that *acid-base phenomena in liquid sulfur dioxide are not limited solely to oxide ion mobility*. It also implies that in the absence of bromide ion, for example, oxide ion transfer between SO_2 molecules is exceedingly slow. Thus, further evidence against the rapid auto-ionization of SO_2 into thionyl and sulfite ions is provided.

5–H   IONIZATION OF THIONYL HALIDES IN LIQUID SULFUR DIOXIDE

Grigg and Lauder (1950) observed that there occurred *no* exchange of ^{18}O between thionyl chloride and sulfur dioxide, even after nine days. This result clearly invalidates the proposed dissociation of thionyl chloride into thionyl ions and chloride ions. One interpretation of this result is that thionyl chloride is a weaker acid than sulfur trioxide and has less tendency to remove an oxide ion from the oxide donor, sulfur dioxide. To account for the non-exchange of sulfur and oxygen between liquid sulfur dioxide and thionyl chloride, the proposed ionic interaction, which involves chloride ion transfer, is

$$SO_2 + SOCl_2 \rightleftarrows SO_2Cl^- + SOCl^+$$

One singular advantage of this proposal is that the equilibrium does not involve doubly-charged ions.

Radiochlorine exchange experiments between tetramethylammonium chloride and thionyl chloride dissolved together in liquid sulfur dioxide have shown that a rapid exchange of chlorine atoms takes place. This means that *some* ionic process involving chloride ions must occur. This *could* involve a dissociation with formation of $SOCl^+$, but exchange could also occur by way of an association equilibrium, e.g.

$$SOCl_2 + Cl^- \rightleftarrows SOCl_3{}^-$$

In order to distinguish between an association and a dissociation mechanism, the exchange of sulfur between $^{35}SOCl_2$ and $SOBr_2$ dissolved in liquid SO_2 was investigated. Sulfur exchange would occur by means of a halide exchange between the two thionyl compounds. The rapid and complete exchange, which *was* observed, indicated that ionization into SOX^+ must occur for either or both thionyl halides. Finally, radiosulfur exchange between liquid sulfur dioxide and excess thionyl chloride was negligible. The proposed ionic process involving the thionyl ion, SO^{+2}, appears to be most unlikely. Additional corroborating experiments have been performed which involve ^{36}Cl exchange in thionyl chloride solutions containing NR_4Cl and antimony trichloride. These data indicate that the ionic species involved are $SOCl^+$ and Cl^-.

All of the discussion in sections 5–G and 5–H emphasizes that although a theory may be consistent with the observed experimental results it may still be incorrect. In the particular instance of the proposed autoionization of liquid SO_2 into SO^{+2} and $S_2O_5^{-2}$ ions, too many conclusions were drawn before an adequate amount of experimental evidence had been accumulated. The need to exercise the proper degree of skepticism is a requisite of every scientist.

5–I SULFUR DIOXIDE IN THE PETROLEUM INDUSTRY

The application of liquid sulfur dioxide to petroleum refining has been discussed in detail by Kalichevsky and Stagner. We shall confine our short discussion to the refining of kerosenes, specifically, with the Edeleanu process for the continuous treatment of light distillates. This process has now been very largely replaced, but through World War II it was of major importance and it does illustrate how nonaqueous chemistry can have an important place in industrial technology.

The distillate to be treated, following drying and the removal of volatile gases, is cooled and pumped into a gas-tight mixer tank. Liquid sulfur dioxide then enters this tank from the top and, being more dense than the hydrocarbon mixture, settles toward the bottom. During the settling process there occurs an intimate mixing of the two liquids. The bottom liquid layer, consisting of liquid sulfur dioxide with its dissolved material, is continuously withdrawn from the bottom of the tank while the raffinate (treated, i.e., purified, liquid) is removed at the top. The streams of cool exit liquids are brought into contact with heat exchangers which, in turn, cool the incoming streams of untreated distillate and fresh liquid sulfur dioxide. The exit liquids then enter multiple evaporators where the sulfur dioxide is easily recovered by distillation, and is then recycled.

During the actual process of refining kerosene the liquid sulfur dioxide dissolves the sulfur compounds, aromatics, and diolefins and leaves, undissolved, the aliphatic and naphthenic compounds. The upper layer, in the tank where the initial mixing takes place, possesses a much lower specific gravity than the original stock while that from the lower layer (sulfur dioxide soluble) has a much higher specific gravity.

Important practical changes in the refined product include: a higher ratio of hydrogen to carbon, which results primarily in an enrichment with respect to saturated compounds; properties approaching those of a kerosene obtained from a paraffin base oil; lower sulfur and nitrogen content; less color; and less smoke when burned.

5–J   ORGANIC REACTIONS IN LIQUID SULFUR DIOXIDE

Certain organic reactions can be advantageously carried out in liquid sulfur dioxide. Most organic compounds dissolve readily in this solvent and the reactions occur at low temperatures thereby eliminating competing side reactions which may occur at higher temperatures.

The solubility of aluminum chloride in liquid sulfur dioxide is sufficient to permit the Friedel-Crafts reaction to be carried out with little difficulty. Secondary reactions which take place in other solvents are largely eliminated in this solvent. The extent of the Fries rearrangement, which is a competing reaction during the conventional preparation of phenolic esters, is greatly reduced. Some examples of the results obtained when the Friedel-Crafts reaction is carried out in this solvent are the conversion of benzene and benzoyl chloride to benzophenone in 84% yield, of phenol and benzoyl chloride to phenylbenzoate in yields of 94%, and of resorcinol and benzoyl chloride to resorcinol dibenzoate in 75% yield.

The use of liquid sulfur dioxide as a solvent for the preparation of carbyl sulfates, as a medium for sulfonation of aromatics, and for halogenation, especially bromination, is discussed by Audrieth and Kleinberg (ref. 2, Ch. 11). The Beckmann rearrangement has been investigated by Tokura and co-workers who have also carried out, recently, many investigations on the polymerization of styrene derivatives in liquid sulfur dioxide (refs. 15, 16). A review on organic reactions in liquid sulfur dioxide by Tokura (ref. 17) has appeared recently.

5–K   THE THEORY OF SOLVENT SYSTEMS AND TRACER EXPERIMENTS IN PHOSGENE

The first substantial evidence on which the theory of solvent systems, or of "ionotropy," was built was obtained with phosgene (carbonyl chloride) as the solvent. A considerable amount of work was carried out with this solvent by Germann (ref. 2, Ch. XII). This investigator, in order to explain the electrical conductivity of solutions of aluminum chloride in phosgene as well as the other chemical properties of such solutions, applied the solvent system concept. He postulated the following ionization processes:

$$COCl_2 \rightleftarrows CO^{+2} + 2\,Cl^-$$

$$COCl_2 + Al_2Cl_6 \rightleftarrows CO^{+2} + 2\,[AlCl_4]^-$$

Since, according to the ionotropic theory, an acid increases the concentration of cations "characteristic of the solvent," aluminum chloride is an acid because it forms divalent carbonyl cations by virtue of the proposed solvolytic reaction. The ready solubility of calcium chloride in such solutions was explained by Germann in terms of the equation

$$[CO^{+2}], 2\,[AlCl_4^-] + CaCl_2 \rightleftarrows [Ca^{+2}], 2\,[AlCl_4^-] + COCl_2$$

The foregoing is a typical "neutralization" reaction according to the solvent system theory. Tracer experiments by Huston (1956, 1957) clearly demonstrated the limitations of the solvent system formulation. The results of these experiments may be summarized. (1) A compound of composition $AlCl_3 \cdot COCl_2$ was isolated from which phosgene was distillable at low pressure; the chlorine atoms of the aluminum chloride and the phosgene are completely nonequivalent. (2) Chloride exchange, which should be rapid if the solvent system ionization scheme were operative, is exceedingly slow. (3) When ionic chlorides were dissolved in such solutions, the ionic chloride went directly to the aluminum chloride without participation of any kind by the solvent. There was no catalysis of solute-solvent exchange.

Thus, we encounter another case in which a theory may satisfactorily explain the facts which have been observed but has been found subsequently to be incorrect.

57

Exercises

1. The topic is "Electrical Conductivity and Ionization in Liquid Sulfur Dioxide Solutions." Discuss the following points:
   a. the ionic dissociation constant of liquid SO_2
   b. conductance of tetraalkylammonium salts
   c. conductance of planar ions
   d. conductance of alkali metal halides
   e. ion-pair formation

2. Describe the details of some of the organic reactions which have been carried out in liquid sulfur dioxide.

3. Prepare a report on one of the following nonprotonic solvents: $SeOCl_2$, $AsCl_3$, $POCl_3$, $NOCl$, BrF_3.

References

1. T. C. Waddington, Ch. 6 of *Non-Aqueous Solvent Systems*, T. C. Waddington, Ed., Academic Press, 1965.
2. L. F. Audrieth and J. Kleinberg, *Non-Aqueous Solvents*, Wiley, 1953.
3. V. A. Kalichevsky and B. A. Stagner, *Chemical Refining of Petroleum*, Reinhold, 1942.
4. G. Jander, *Die Chemie in Wasserähnlichen Lösungsmitteln*, Springer-Verlag, Berlin, 1949.
5. L. C. Bateman, E. D. Hughes, and C. K. Ingold, *J. Chem. Soc.*, 243 (1944).
6. T. H. Norris, *J. Phys. Chem.*, **63,** 383 (1959).
7. J. L. Huston, *ibid.*, **63,** 389 (1959).
8. J. L. Huston, *J. Inorg. Nucl. Chem.*, **2,** 128 (1956).
9. J. L. Huston, and C. E. Lang, *ibid.*, **4,** 30 (1957).
10. R. E. Johnson, T. H. Norris, and J. L. Huston, *J. Am. Chem. Soc.*, **73,** 3052 (1951).
11. J. L. Huston, *ibid.*, **73,** 3049 (1951).
12. S. Nakata, *J. Chem. Soc. Japan*, **64,** 635 (1943).
13. E. C. M. Grigg and I. Lauder, *Trans. Faraday Soc.*, **46,** 1039 (1950).
14. N. N. Lichtin, "Liquid Sulfur Dioxide," in Vol. I, *Progress in Physical Organic Chemistry*, S. G. Cohen, A. Streitwieser, Jr., and R. W. Taft, Eds., Wiley, 1963.
15. R. Tada, Y. Masubuchi, and N. Tokura, *Bull. Chem. Soc. Japan*, **34,** 209 (1961); N. Tokura and K. Shiina, *ibid.*, **35,** 1779 (1962); N. Tokura, K. Shiina, and T. Terashima, *ibid.*, **35,** 1986 (1962).
16. N. Tokura, M. Matsuda, and Y. Ogawa, *J. Polymer Sci.*, Pt. A. **1**(8), 2965 (1963).
17. N. Tokura, *Yuki Gosei Kagaku Kyokai Shi*, **21,** (8), 598 (1963).

CHAPTER **6**

Liquid-Liquid Solvent Extraction

6–A SOME HISTORICAL BACKGROUND

The distribution of a solute species between two immiscible liquid phases has long furnished a useful technique for the separation and purification of organic materials. However, this technique was not widely used in inorganic chemistry until quite recently. The great demand for uranium during the development of the nuclear bomb led to an intensive and large scale investigation and the subsequent application of liquid-liquid solvent extraction to the separation and purification of inorganic species.

The demand for uranium is now limited, but this situation may soon be reversed with the rapidly growing use of nuclear energy as a source of electric power. Solvent extraction has played an extremely important role in the extraction of uranium from its ores in which it is usually present in concentrations less than one percent. This means that a very large quantity of ore must be processed in order to recover from it a sufficient quantity of the desired metal.

For over a hundred years it was well known that uranyl nitrate, $UO_2(NO_3)_2$, could be extracted from its aqueous solution into ethyl ether. However, because it is both flammable and explosive, ethyl ether is not a desirable solvent for use on a commercial scale. The search for other suitable solvents led to the discovery and application of tri-*n*-butylphosphate, commonly known as **TBP**, as a substitute for ethyl ether

$$C_4H_9O-\underset{\underset{OC_4H_9}{|}}{\overset{\overset{OC_4H_9}{|}}{P}}=O$$

TBP

TBP has many of the assets of ethyl ether, but it has a low vapor pressure and very limited tendency to either burn or explode.

Early in the development of TBP, it was observed that its ability to extract uranium from sulfuric acid solutions increased as the solutions aged. It was soon discovered that this was due to the hydrolysis of the tributyl ester to the dibutylphosphoric acid ester which is the more efficient extractive reagent. This observation led to a study of other esters of phosphoric acid which showed that the di-2-ethylhexylphosphoric acid ester, abbreviated HDEHP, is an extremely effective reagent for solvent extraction. Its formula is

$$\left[CH_3-CH_2-CH_2-CH_2-\underset{\underset{C_2H_5}{|}}{CH}-CH_2-O- \right]_2 \overset{\overset{O}{||}}{P}-OH$$

HDEHP

6–B   GENERAL CONSIDERATIONS

A solute can be extracted from a liquid phase into another liquid phase, only if it is more soluble in the second than in the first. This increased solubility in the second phase is usually brought about by the coordination of the solute with the solvent molecules. For example, the extraction of uranyl nitrate from water into TBP can be described by the following equation

$$UO_2^{+2} + 2\,NO_3^- + 2\,TBP \rightleftarrows UO_2(NO_3)_2 \cdot 2\,TBP$$

In this case, but not always, the same material serves as the coordinating agent and the solvent. In many cases, the water-immiscible organic phase consists of two components, one of which is the water-immiscible solvent, while the second is a substance which is extremely soluble in the organic phase, but insoluble in the aqueous phase. The water-immiscible solvent is often referred to as the *diluent*, especially when it does not act as a coordinating agent. The second component, which forms a coordination compound with the metal ion and which is soluble in the organic phase, is referred to as the *reagent*, the *extractant* and, when it is dissolved in a nonpolar, noncoordinating diluent, it is even referred to as the *solvent*. For example, HDEHP is ordinarily employed in solutions in kerosene. The kerosene serves as the diluent while HDEHP is the reagent, or solvent. There arises a certain ambiguity in the use of these terms and also some confusion. However, this terminology has been accepted and is widely used.

Another well-known reagent is thenoyltrifluoroacetone, TTA. Its structure is

TTA

This reagent is used for the extraction of a variety of metal ions from water into a number of different solvents. Beryllium ion, for example, forms the compound $Be(TTA)_2$* which can be extracted into xylene. In this case the xylene is the diluent, while TTA is the reagent (solvent). In reading the literature on solvent extraction, it is important to remember that the terms solvent and diluent may have different meanings.

If a dissolved species distributes itself between two phases, and if it has the same chemical form in both phases, the ratio of the concentrations of the dissolved species in the two phases is described by the "partition law"

$$P = (C)_o/(C)_a = \text{constant}$$

where P is called the *partition coefficient*. In the systems which we shall discuss, the water-immiscible organic reagent is contained in the organic phase for the express purpose of forming a complex which is soluble in the organic phase. This makes the partition law inapplicable. The nature of the dissolved species in the two phases will

---

* Here TTA refers to the anion derived from the molecule shown previously.

be, of necessity, different and the ratio of their concentrations cannot be constant.

Let D represent the *distribution ratio* (sometimes called the *extraction coefficient*)

Let $(X)_o = (X_1)_o + (X_2)_o + \ldots (X_i)_o$, i.e., total concentration of all species X in all chemical forms in the organic phase, and

let $(X)_a = (X_1)_a + (X_2)_a + \ldots (X_i)_a$, i.e., total concentration of all species X in all chemical forms in the aqueous phase.

Then, $D = (X)_o/(X)_a$

Since D varies with such parameters as the reagent concentration, *pH*, metal ion concentration, etc., which can be experimentally controlled, it is a very useful quantity in understanding the nature of extraction systems.

6–C   DISTRIBUTION OF THE SOLUTE IN THE FORM OF NEUTRAL MOLECULES

There are a few systems in which inorganic compounds are extracted directly from their aqueous solutions into relatively inert solvents without strong solvation. The most familiar example of this type of system is the distribution of iodine between carbon tetrachloride and water. It was studied as early as 1896 (Jakowkin) and quite recently by Davies and Gwynne (1952). The partition coefficient of I_2 is given by

$$P = (I_2)_o/(I_2)_a$$

The partition coefficient must be determined experimentally under conditions in which no hydrolysis of I_2 to I_3^- occurs in the aqueous phase. Jakowkin obtained a value for P of 85–88 at 25°C while Davies and Gwynne selected 89.6 as a best value for this constant. In this particular system, as in so many others, chemical changes may directly affect the nature and the concentrations of the species which distribute. The presence of iodide in the aqueous phase results in the equilibrium

$$I_2 + I^- \rightleftarrows I_3^-$$

Davies and Gwynne maintained a $(I_2)/[(I_3^-) + (I^-)]$ ratio of 7–350 in their experiments. Since essentially all of the iodide is converted to I_3^- by the excess iodine, the reasonable assumption was made that in dilute solutions the only species in the aqueous phase were I_2 and

I_3^-, and in the organic phase, I_2. The distribution ratio can then be written as

$$D = (I_2)_o/[(I_2)_a + (I_3^-)_a]$$

D can also be written in terms of the partition coefficient and K, the formation constant for the $I_2 + I^- \rightleftarrows I_3^-$ equilibrium, as

$$D = P/[1 + K(I^-)]$$

From a knowledge of P and by experimentally measuring D, Davies and Gwynne were able to evaluate K. This type of experiment illustrates how distribution measurements can be used for the determination of formation constants. At high concentrations of iodine the equilibrium becomes more complicated. In addition to the formation of polyiodides as high as I_{14}^{-2} in the aqueous phase, association of the iodine molecules in the organic phase must also be considered.

Other systems of this type include the extraction, by heptane, of iodine and iodine cyanide from their aqueous solutions and of the halides of mercury(II) by benzene.

6–D EXTRACTION OF HALOMETALLIC ACIDS

Among the most familiar and most widely studied solvent extraction systems are those involving the extraction of metal ions, especially transition metal ions, from acid solutions containing excess halide ions.

One of the first known and what has been the most widely studied of these systems is that which deals with the extraction of ferric chloride from hydrochloric acid solutions by ethers. For many years it was mistakenly assumed that the iron was extracted into the ether phase as molecular ferric chloride. As is evident from Figure 6–1, the distribution ratio shows an initial rapid increase with increasing concentration of hydrochloric acid. Maxima are then noted which are followed by decreases in the distribution ratio. These maxima have been attributed to extraction of acid and the concurrent formation of nonextractable higher chloro complexes.

It was eventually recognized that the species entering the organic phase was not molecular ferric chloride, but the acid complex $HFeCl_4$. It is generally agreed that no primary solvation of the iron takes place, and that what actually is involved is hydration of the proton and secondary solvation.

63

The steep rise in the distribution ratio with the initial increase in hydrochloric acid concentration noted in Figure 6–1 can be explained in terms of increasing formation of extractable $HFeCl_4$ complex. The occurrence of the maximum and the subsequent decrease with further increase in aqueous hydrochloric acid concentration cannot be explained in terms of the formation of higher nonextracting iron(III) complexes since no complex higher than $FeCl_4^-$ is known. Furthermore, this maximum occurs at a higher initial acid concentration when diisopropyl ether rather than ethyl ether is the solvent and it does not occur at all when bis(2-chloroethyl) ether is the solvent.

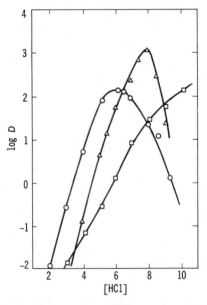

Figure 6–1 The logarithm of the distribution ratio plotted against the molar concentration of HCl for the extraction of iron(III) chloride into ethyl ether, ∘; into isopropyl ether, △; and into bis(2-chloroethyl) ether, □. (From Diamond and Tuck, ref. 1.)

When diethyl ether is the solvent the most widely accepted explanation is that as the hydrochloric acid concentration increases there is extracted into the aqueous phase a great deal of ether which solvates the hydrogen ion in that phase. This transfer of the organic solvent into the water phase occurs to such a large degree in concentrated acid solutions that a very significant change in the aqueous phase volume occurs. Isopropyl ether is so much less water-soluble than diethyl ether that the maximum occurs at a significantly higher hydrochloric acid concentration. In the case of very slightly soluble ethers, e.g., the di-*n*-butyl- and bis(2-chloroethyl) derivatives, their solubilities in the aqueous acid are so limited that no significant volume changes occur and the aqueous solution remains essentially undiluted. Hence, no maxima are noted.

Friedman (1952) compared the absorption spectra of iron(III) as extracted from hydrochloric acid in a number of ether and ether-like solvents with that of solid $KFeCl_4$ and concluded that the iron species do not vary from solvent to solvent. This furnishes very strong evidence that the solvent is not coordinated directly to the iron. Similar studies which deal with the extraction of indium(III) from hydrobromic acid solutions by ethyl ether and methyl isobutyl ketone have been carried out. The extracted species in this case is $HInBr_4$.

One of the explanations which has been put forth to interpret the relatively high extraction of these metals as complex anions is that the halide ions form an insulating shell about the central metal ion which inhibits primary hydration. Thus, there exist relatively weak water-metal ion interactions because of the formation of the relatively large univalent tetrahalometal anion. Structurally, these anions resemble carbon tetrachloride and they have a great tendency to be forced out of the aqueous phase into the relatively structureless organic solvent. The geometry of the ion, viz. large size and low charge, becomes an increasingly important factor in the understanding of these solvent extraction systems. Polyvalent anions such as $CoCl_4^{-2}$ and $ZnCl_4^{-2}$ show very limited extraction into ether. The size of the cation is also important. The presence of large ions of low charge, e.g., tetraphenylarsonium or tetrabutylammonium ion, greatly enhances the extraction into the ether layer.

The ion-dipole attraction between a water molecule and a divalent ion must be considerably stronger than the corresponding interaction with a large univalent ion. Hence the limited extraction of the divalent ions is consistent with their stronger association with the solvent water molecules. The enhancement of the extraction by large univalent ions may result from the ion-pairing type of behavior proposed by Diamond (1963). In this view, both the large univalent cation, e.g., the tetraphenylarsonium ion, and the relatively large univalent anion, e.g., tetrachloroferrate(III) are only weakly hydrophilic. The strongly hydrogen-bonded water structure forces them together so as to maximize water-water interactions and minimize the disturbance due to their presence. The water would favor rejection of this large ion-pair since the "hole" remaining following its rejection is replaced by the strongly hydrogen-bonded water structure.

The question of whether neutral species such as $MA_3(H_2O)_3$ are extracted to any considerable degree is not yet settled. If the organic solvent molecules possess strong donor tendencies, the metal may be solvated directly to form the octahedral species MA_3S_3 where S represents the solvent donor molecule. Whether such reactions occur to any degree depends very much upon the tendency of the metal ion to assume and retain an octahedral coordination. As is often the case with experimental investigations, discrepancies are encountered when one attempts to explain an extraction entirely in terms of the single species HMX_4. When such discrepancies have been observed, the formation of competing octahedral species has been one of the explanations invoked. The fact that many metals extract very poorly as the fluoride complexes supports this view. Ferric ion, for example, in the presence of fluoride, forms FeF_6^{-3} and reaches its larger coordination number. Not only is this ion smaller than that formed with the other halides, but it also bears a multiple negative charge. Both of these factors contribute to its decreased extractability.

In this section, mention should be made of the dependence of D on the metal concentration as it is affected by polymerization of the metal species in one or both phases. This type of behavior usually involves aggregation in solvents having low dielectric constants or it may be the result of the formation of nonextractable polymeric species in the aqueous phase. Such behavior may be illustrated by the extraction of molybdenum(VI) as the chloride from 4 M hydrochloric acid (Figure 6–2). The decrease in D which begins at ca. $10^{-3}M$ Mo(VI) is due to the formation of nonextractable polymeric molybdenum species in the aqueous phase.

6–E   ORGANOPHOSPHORUS COMPOUNDS AS EXTRACTANTS

Organophosphorus compounds have been used with great success on a commercial scale in nuclear technology. They have been employed in the treatment of raw materials, e.g., in the extraction of uranium from its ores, and for fission product separation. They have been so widely studied that a separate discussion is warranted. In a recent review, Peppard (1966) has classified phosphorus-based extractants into three major groups. These are neutral molecules such as TBP; monoacidic molecules such as HDEHP; and diacidic molecules such as the monoalkylphosphoric acids, $(RO)PO(OH)_2$.

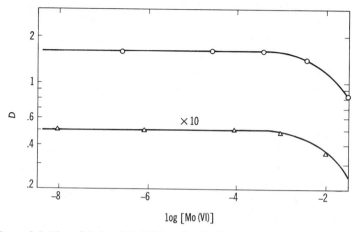

Figure 6–2   Plot of the log [Mo(VI)] *vs.* the distribution coefficient for the extraction of Mo(VI) from 4.1M HCl into ethyl ether, ∘; and bis(2-chloroethyl) ether, △. (From Diamond and Tuck, ref. 1.)

In section 6–A it was mentioned that the hydrolytic product of TBP, di-*n*-butylphosphoric acid was found to be a more effective reagent for the extraction of uranium than TBP itself. From subsequent investigations with this group of compounds, di-(2-ethylhexyl)phosphoric acid, HDEHP, emerged as the single, most important reagent. A discussion of the application of this reagent to fission product recovery has been presented recently (Horner, et al., 1963). The following discussion will describe in some detail the extraction of U(VI) from acid perchlorate solutions by this reagent in hexane solutions (Baes, Zingaro and Coleman, 1958).

Figure 6–3 shows the dependence of the uranium distribution ratio at low uranium concentrations on the reagent concentration (HDEHP)$_o$ and on the aqueous acidity (H$^+$). The very close agreement of the points with lines of slope 2 on the log-log plot suggests that D is directly proportional to the square of the HDEHP concentration and inversely proportional to the square of the aqueous acidity. This implies that each uranyl ion extracted into the organic phase forms a complex with two HDEHP molecules and that two moles of hydrogen ion enter the aqueous phase for each mole of uranium which enters the organic phase. The exchange of two pro-

67

tons for each uranyl ion extracted was confirmed by analytical determination of the aqueous acid concentration before and after extraction.

Equilibrium vapor pressure measurements on HDEHP-*n*-hexane solutions showed that HDEHP was dimeric throughout the concentration range studied. In view of this, the dependence of D on the square of the HDEHP concentration means that each extracted uranyl ion reacts with two dimers and the resulting complex contains the equivalent of two HDEHP molecules in addition to two anions

$$UO_{2(a)}^{+2} + 2 \, (HDEHP)_{2(o)} \rightleftarrows UO_2H_2 \, (DEHP)_{4(o)} + 2 \, H_{(a)}^{+} \qquad (1)$$

Since the distribution ratio is independent of uranium concentration (Figure 6–3 and linear portions of Figure 6–4), no polynuclear uranium species need be considered at these metal concentrations.

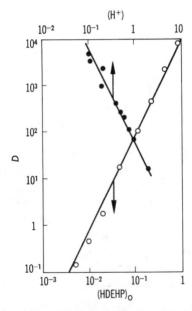

Figure 6–3 The dependence of uranium(VI) extraction from aqueous HClO₄-NaClO₄ solutions by HDEHP in hexane on HDEHP concentration, ○, and on acidity, ●, at 25°. The lines are drawn with slopes of +2 and −2, respectively. The HDEHP variation measurements were made at $1\,M$ acidity with the equilibrium uranium concentration in the organic phase in the range 10^{-4} to $7 \times 10^{-3}M$, varying from 0.7–6.2% of the HDEHP concentration. The acidity variation measurements were made at $0.1\,M$ HDEHP with the concentration of the uranium in the organic phase at 0.0040-$0.0047M$. (From Baes, Zingaro, and Coleman, ref. 7.)

The equilibrium quotient for the reaction in equation 1 may be written

$$K = [(U)_o(H^+)^2]/(U)_a \{[(HDEHP)_o - 4(U)_o]/2\}^2$$
$$= 4 D(H^+)^2/\{(HDEHP)_o - [4(U)_o]\}^2 \qquad (2)$$

The effect of increasing the concentration of uranium in the organic phase is shown by the equilibrium curves for 0.1 and 0.01 M HDEHP in Figure 6–4. There are plotted experimental (dashed lines), and calculated (solid lines) values, over a range of aqueous acidities.

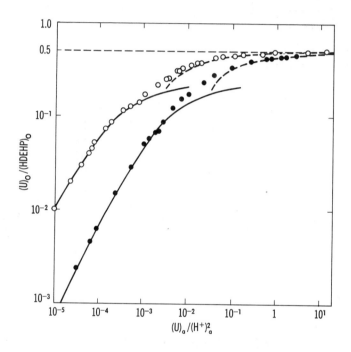

Figure 6–4 The extraction of uranium(VI) from aqueous HClO$_4$-NaClO$_4$ solution by HDEHP in hexane as a function of aqueous uranium concentration [normalized to $1M$ (H$^+$)] at 25°. 0.1M HDEHP, ○; 0.01M HDEHP, •. The horizontal dashed curve corresponds to a uranium(VI)-HDEHP ratio of 0.5. The solid curves were calculated by means of Equation 6 ($K = 4 \times 10^4$ at 0.1M HDEHP; $K = 2.8 \times 10^4$ at 0.01M HDEHP); the dashed curves were calculated by means of Equation 7. (From Baes, Zingaro and Coleman, ref. 7.)

While the results at low uranium concentrations are consistent with the reaction in equation 1, other species are formed at higher uranium concentrations leading to a limiting uranium-HDEHP ratio of

1:2.   The dashed curves in Figure 6–4 show that in the range $(U)_o/(HDEHP)_o = 0.3$ to 0.5, the extractions conform to the empirical relation

$$0.5 - [(U)_o/(HDEHP)_o] = 0.0053/[(HDEHP)_o(U)_a/(H^+)^2]^{1/2} \quad \text{(3)}$$

Above $(U)_o/(HDEHP)_o = 0.25$, vapor pressure measurements indicate that complexes in the organic phase are increasingly polymeric in uranium.   Evidence for such polymerization with increasing uranium saturation is shown quite dramatically by the abrupt increase in the viscosities of HDEHP solutions in *n*-hexane as $(U)_o/(HDEHP)$ is increased beyond 0.45, Figure 6–5.

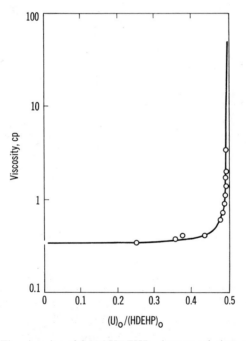

Figure 6–5   The viscosity of $0.1M$ HDEHP-*n*-hexane solutions as a function of uranium(VI) content at 25°.   (From Baes, Zingaro, and Coleman, ref. 7.)

Electron micrographs of HDEHP-hexane solutions nearly saturated with uranium show extended fibers which suggest a long chain polymeric structure.   A suggested formulation gives uranium a coordination number of eight by sharing of the oxygen atoms between uranyl ions.   In this view, the formulation for the 1:4 complex, I, and the

70

polymeric chains $(UO_2)_nX_{2n+2}H_2$, II, would be

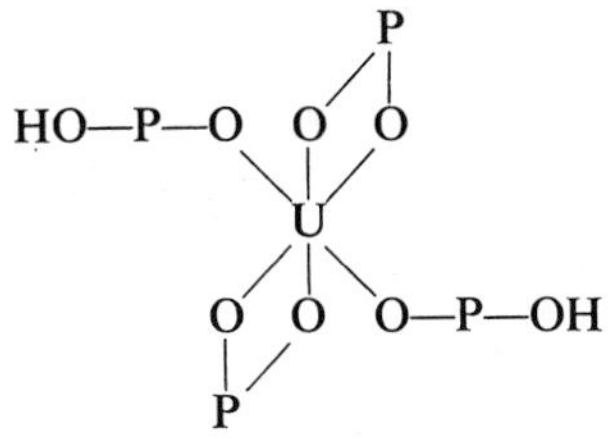

I

and

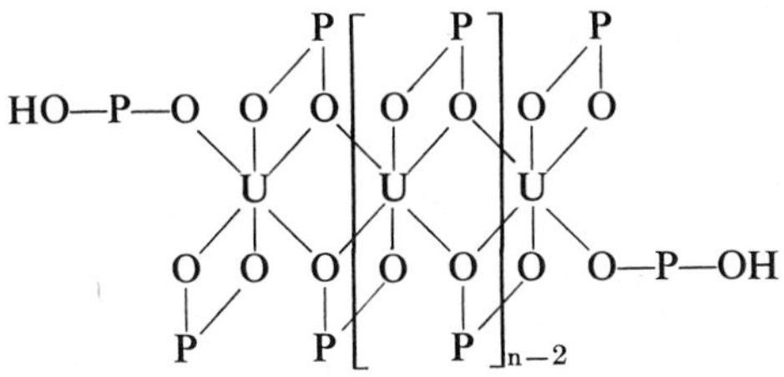

II

In structures I and II, each U is a uranyl, UO_2^{+2} ion, thus giving the metal a coordination number of 8. Each P-containing entity is actually an $(RO)_2P(O)O^-$ ion, where R is the 2-ethylhexyl group.

6–F ALKALI METAL ION SEPARATION BY LIQUID-LIQUID SOLVENT EXTRACTION

The alkali metals, as a group, are among the most difficult to separate from each other. They have little tendency to form either insoluble compounds or complex ions, and these are the chemical "handles" most widely used for metal ion separations. The isotope ^{137}Cs, which possesses a half-life in excess of 30 years, has presented an especially serious problem in fission product separation. The interesting reagent 4-*sec*-butyl-2-(α-methylbenzyl)phenol, usually refer-red to as **BAMBP**, shows promise as a reagent for the recovery of cesi-um from ore leach liquors as well as in the separation of radioactive cesium from other reactor fuel fission products.

In searching for a reagent that would extract cesium ions, the ability of the phenolic cation resins to exchange alkali metal ions was taken into account. Over a hundred phenols were screened and **BAMBP** was found to possess the most desirable overall properties. Its structure, referred to in the equations to follow as ROH, is

We can write a generalized equation for the extraction of cesium into carbon tetrachloride solutions as follows

$$Cs^+ + n(ROH)_{(o)} + OH^- \rightleftharpoons CsOR \cdot (n - 1)ROH_{(o)} + H_2O_{(a)} \qquad (4)$$

for which the concentration equilibrium quotient can be written as

$$K_2 = \frac{[CsOR \cdot (n - 1)ROH][H_2O]}{[Cs^+][ROH]^n[OH^-]} \qquad (5)$$

Since $[H_2O]$ is essentially constant and if we define the distribution ratio

$$D = \frac{(Cs) \text{ in the organic phase}}{(Cs) \text{ in the aqueous phase}} \qquad (6)$$

we can write

$$K_2 = D/(ROH)^n(OH^-) \qquad (7)$$

This, when placed in logarithmic form becomes

$$\log D = n \log (ROH) + \log (OH^-) + \log K_2 \qquad (8)$$

K_2 is already a constant and the other terms, viz., (ROH) or (OH^-) can be controlled experimentally. For example, if tracer level concentrations of ^{137}Cs are used, i.e., $(Cs^+) \sim 10^{-8}M$, extraction of Cs will cause no significant changes either in the reagent concentration or in the *pH*.

Log *D* was found to increase linearly with slope 1.0 with increasing *pH* (at constant [ROH]) indicating that the proton of the phenol is exchanged for a cesium ion. In Figure 6–6, log *D* has been plotted against the log of the reagent concentration. Curve (1), which represents extraction data employing the formal reagent concentration, possesses a slope of 2.8. Infrared studies showed that the reagent is associated, with the dimer being the only associated species present

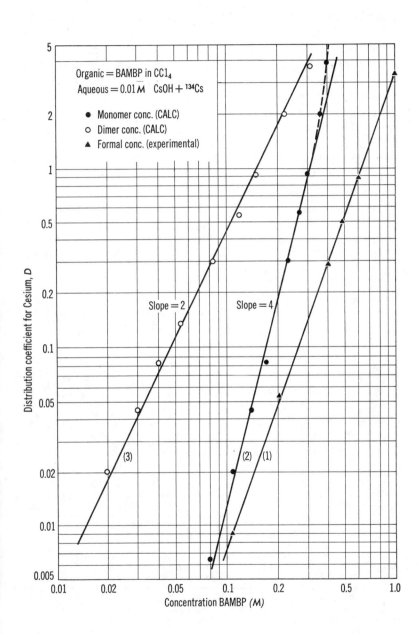

Figure 6–6 Reagent dependence of cesium extraction. (From Egan, Zingaro, and Benjamin, ref. 9.)

in significant concentrations. From both the infrared and ultraviolet spectra the fraction of reagent present as monomer and dimer in solutions of various concentrations was calculated. In curves (2) and (3) of Figure 6–6, the log D is plotted as a function of the monomer and dimer concentrations and the slopes of the lines correspond very closely to values of 4 and 2, respectively.

In Figure 6–7 are plotted isotherms for the extraction of alkali metals from aqueous solutions of their hydroxides by 1 M solutions of BAMBP. Lithium and sodium isotherms are not plotted since extraction of these ions did not take place at hydroxide ion concentrations $\leqq$ 1 M. This means that separation of Cs from Na is essentially quantitative, provided that the extraction is carried out at aqueous hydroxide concentrations $\leqq$ 1 M. For Rb and Cs, their concentrations in the organic phase approach a value of 0.25 M and then increase abruptly to higher values. At organic metal ion concentrations below 0.25 M, the water concentrations are the same as those

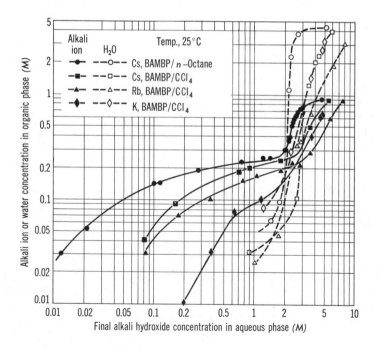

Figure 6–7 Alkali metal ion extraction isotherms. BAMBP = 1M. (From Egan, Zingaro, and Benjamin, ref. 9.)

obtained in 1 M BAMBP in the absence of any metal ions. Following the marked increase in metal ion concentrations at levels above 0.25 M, there is observed a similarly sharp increase in water content.

(1) Extraction Chemistry

The first power pH dependence of the cesium extraction coefficient shows that the extraction reaction involves the exchange of Cs^+ with the H^+ of the phenol. This is corroborated by the decrease in intensity of the O—H stretching band of the phenol when cesium is present in the organic phase.

For the average third power reagent dependence (Figure 6–6) to be consistent with an observed ratio of four moles of BAMBP per mole of cesium (Figure 6–7), it is necessary that the reagent be associated. The linearity and observed slopes of the curves in Figure 6–6 suggest that the reactions involved are

$$2\,ROH_{(o)} \rightleftarrows (ROH)_{2(o)} \tag{9}$$

$$Cs^+ + 4\,ROH_{(o)} + OH^- \rightleftarrows CsOR \cdot 3ROH + H_2O \tag{10}$$

$$Cs^+ + 2\,(ROH)_{2(o)} + OH^- \rightleftarrows CsOR \cdot 3ROH_{(o)} + H_2O \tag{11}$$

As the reagent concentration decreases, the monomer becomes the predominant species, and the equilibrium described by equation 10 predominates. At formal reagent concentrations greater than 0.2 M (dotted portion of the monomer curve, Figure 6–6), the curves converge rapidly and the dimer equilibrium (eq. 11) predominates.

Accordingly, a fourth power reagent dependence of the extraction coefficient would be expected in dilute solutions, and a second power reagent dependence would be expected in concentrated solutions. Curve (1) in Figure 6–6 would therefore be expected to show a change in slope from a limiting value of four at the lower reagent concentrations to a limiting value of two at the higher concentrations. The plot of the experimental points yielded a line of slope 2.8 which is close to an average of the other two slopes.

The abrupt change in the extraction isotherm (Figure 6–7) indicates a marked change in the extraction mechanism when the cesium concentration reaches and passes 0.25 M in the 1 M BAMBP. The ease of extraction of all of the alkali metal ions by BAMBP at very high aqueous hydroxide ion concentrations, where water is co-extracted, results from a large shift to the right in the equilibrium given by

$$M^+(H_2O)_x + OH^- + ROH \rightleftarrows M^+OR^-(H_2O)_y + (x - y + 1)H_2O \tag{12}$$

75

In the case of carbon tetrachloride solutions containing cesium ion, y approaches a limiting value of four (Figure 6–7).

(2) Basis of Extraction

The ability of BAMBP to extract cesium to the exclusion of the smaller ions in the water-free equilibrium systems is due in part to the extremely small hydration energy which needs to be overcome. Also, the transfer of the largest ions would be favored by the decrease in free energy resulting from rejection of the large univalent ion by the disrupted aqueous phase and reformation of the normal water structure following its expulsion. In addition, the larger ions can associate with more extractant molecules, giving a species which is more compatible with the organic phase.

(3) Nature of the Extracted Species

Because cesium is a very large ion of low charge and possesses very little tendency to coordinate, one possible species in the organic phase is an ion pair. Such an ion pair might be simply the cesium phenolate, itself, or a cesium-anion polymer, i.e., $Cs^+[RO(ROH)_n]^-$, where n is a small integer. However, the experimental evidence emphasizes the four to one stoichiometry and suggests a cesium ion solvated by four phenol molecules. In this view, the extraction of water at cesium concentrations greater than $0.25\ M$ involves replacement of BAMBP molecules by water, ultimately resulting in a hydrated cesium ion associated with a phenolate anion. This picture is also supported by the experimental fact that the amount of water extracted per metal ion decreases in the order $Na^+ > K^+ > Rb^+ > Cs^+$. In view of the established stability of the dimeric species in hindered phenols, a structure which involves solvation by hydrogen-bonded dimers is highly plausible. This suggested structure maintains the hydrogen bonds between pairs of the solvating phenol molecules. Since a

$$
\begin{array}{c}
\text{R—O—H---O—R} \\
\searrow\ \swarrow\quad\searrow \\
\text{Cs}^+\qquad \text{H} \\
\nearrow\quad\nwarrow \\
\text{R—O---H—O—R}
\end{array}
$$

single acid proton resonance is observed in nuclear magnetic resonance studies, all acidic protons are equivalent, and hence are in rapid exchange. This structure fits the extraction nuclear magnetic resonance, and infrared data, and suggests an energetic contribution to the extraction by preserving the phenol dimer bonds.

6–G OTHER REAGENTS OF IMPORTANCE

Many reagents extract metals because they form chelated complexes. Some of the more commonly known chelating reagents are TTA, β-diketones, hydroxyaldehydes and amino acids. This category includes thousands of organic reagents which find wide-spread analytical applications. The volume by Morrison and Freiser deals with this subject in detail.

Another large group of important extractants includes amines and basic quaternary ammonium salts. Many amines such as quinoline, 8-hydroxyquinoline, α-, and α'-dipryidyl have been used for specific analytical purposes. Long chain amines have found important commercial applications both in the recovery of uranium from ore leech liquors and in fission product separation (ref. 4).

Exercises

1. Report on the separation of indium and gallium from aluminum by solvent extraction as their 2-methyl 8-hydroxyquinoline complexes.
2. Discuss the meaning of the term "synergism" as it applies to the solvent extraction of metal ions.
3. Discuss the metallurgy of uranium. Begin with the raw ore and discuss the methods and techniques used to separate the various metallic components with particular emphasis on final purification steps which utilize either TBP or long chain amines.
4. Why is it more efficient to contact the phase which is to be extracted a number of times (n) with equal volumes of the extracting phase rather than a single time with a large volume equal to (nV)?

References

1. R. M. Diamond and D. G. Tuck, "Extraction of Inorganic Compounds into Organic Solvents," in Vol. 2, *Progress in Inorganic Chemistry*, F. A. Cotton, Ed., Interscience, 1960.
2. Y. Marcus, *Chem. Revs.*, **63**, 139 (1963).
3. G. H. Morrison and H. Freiser, *Solvent Extraction in Analytical Chemistry*, John Wiley, 1957.
4. C. F. Coleman, "Amines as Extractants—Survey of the Descriptive and Fundamental Extraction Chemistry," U.S. At. Energy Comm., ORNL-3516 (1963).

5. H. L. Friedman, *J. Am. Chem. Soc.*, **74,** 5 (1952).
6. D. E. Horner, D. J. Crouse, K. B. Brown, and B. Weaver, *Nuclear Science and Engineering*, **17,** 234 (1963).
7. C. F. Baes, Jr., R. A. Zingaro, and C. F. Coleman, *J. Phys. Chem.*, **62,** 129 (1958).
8. R. M. Diamond, *ibid.*, **67,** 2513 (1963).
9. B. Z. Egan, R. A. Zingaro, and B. M. Benjamin, *Inorg. Chem.*, **4,** 1055 (1965).
10. A. A. Jakowkin, *Z. physik. Chem.*, **20,** 19 (1896).
11. M. Davies and E. Gwynne, *J. Am. Chem. Soc.*, **74,** 2748 (1952).
12. D. F. Peppard, *Advances in Inorganic and Radiochemistry*, Vol. 9, H. J. Emeléus and A. G. Sharpe, Eds., Academic Press, 1966.

CHAPTER **7**

Fused Salt Systems

7–A   GENERAL CONSIDERATIONS

One area of nonaqueous solvents research which has been dealt with in organized textbook form only recently is that which concerns the chemistry of fused salt systems (Sundheim, 1964; Corbett and Duke, 1963; Blander, 1964). Examination of the published literature on fused salts reveals that these systems have been treated very largely from the physico-chemical approach. They have not been studied, to any significant degree, as media for chemical reactions. A great deal of new and exciting synthetic chemistry should be possible in these solvents.

Water, a solvent of high dielectric constant and high polarity, is the medium in which the vast majority of inorganic chemical reactions is performed. Ionic salts, for example, potassium nitrate, present us with the opportunity to carry out reactions in media of high dielectric constant at much higher temperatures than is possible in water. When one thinks about the large number of ionic crystalline solids which are available, their high melting temperatures and the wide range of temperature over which they exist in the liquid state, one is truly impressed by their potential as media for high temperature reactions. In Table 7–1 are tabulated the melting points of some salts and eutectics.

Table 7–1

*Melting Point of Some Salts and Eutectics Which Have Been Used in Molten Salt Chemistry**

	T_f, °C
$NaNO_3$-KNO_3 (50 mole-%)	223
$LiNO_3$-KNO_3 (44 mole-% KNO_3)	125
$LiNO_3$, $NaNO_3$, KNO_3 (eutectic)	120
LiCl-KCl (~45% LiCl)	352
KF-KCl (eutectic)	605
$NaCl$-$CaCl_2$ (40% NaCl)	560
LiF	1121
LiCl	883
LiBr	823
CsCl	918
CsBr	909

7–B   SOME EXPERIMENTAL TECHNIQUES USED IN FUSED SALT RESEARCH

This subject cannot be dealt with in any great detail because of the limitations of space, but it is possible to introduce a few of the basic experimental procedures.

Some of the problems which face the experimentalist in the fused salt field are readily apparent. All materials of construction must be able to withstand high temperatures for prolonged periods and they must be resistant to chemical attack by the molten salt. Also, there is the problem of furnishing heat to the system. This heat must be carefully controlled and uniformly distributed. For the latter purpose resistance heating is preferred and is the most widely used. At temperatures to 1175°C Nichrome windings can be used; up to 1600°C platinum heaters may be constructed; molybdenum is needed to achieve temperatures as high as 1800°C. For the temperature range 2000–2700°C the use of heaters made of tungsten, tantalum, or molybdenum has been described, but these must be operated in a vacuum in order to avoid atmospheric corrosion, which can be a serious problem at these temperatures.

---

* Melting points of other salts will be found in Table 7–3.

A considerable amount of fused salt chemistry can be carried out in conventional hard glass or fused silica containers. However, the use of the higher melting and more reactive melts requires that containers be constructed of other materials. Among metals used for the construction of reaction vessels are molybdenum, tungsten and tantalum, while refractory oxides, nitrides, carbides and sulfides also find wide application.

(1) Preparation and Purification of Materials

As is typical with other nonaqueous solvents, the most frequent and troublesome impurities in fused salts are water and hydrolytic products. Vacuum techniques and dry-boxes are commonly seen in operations with fused salts, but the most desirable set-up is a completely closed system operating under an inert atmosphere. Purification of salts is preferably and most effectively carried out prior to their fusion. In some cases, it is easier to prepare the salt rather than to purify and dry the purchased product. For example, metal halides have been prepared by the reaction of the very pure metal with the very pure halogen. When this procedure is carried out in a closed system, it gives a much drier product than can be obtained from the commercially available halide.

The most extensively studied melts are probably the alkali and alkaline earth metal halides. They have been widely used either alone or as eutectics. Among the more common of the latter are LiCl-KCl and NaCl-KCl. Alkali metal nitrate mixtures have also been investigated. Molten fluoride chemistry has been the subject of considerable study in connection with the molten salt nuclear reactor.

(2) Physical Measurements in Molten Salts

These include determinations of vapor pressure, heats of fusion and mixing, density, surface tension, electrode potentials, electrical conductivity, absorption spectra and X-ray and electron diffractions. Considerable experimental ingenuity is required to carry out such measurements in fused salt systems. We shall not be able to describe the many clever techniques which have been developed, nor give proper recognition to the many investigators who are responsible for them. Let us, however, look at a few examples.

(3) Vapor Pressure Measurements

In 1919, Ruff and Bergdahl originated a method for the measurement of boiling points which is useful over the range of 900–1500°C and which continues to be widely applied. In this method the rate at which the mass of a sample changes is measured as the temperature or pressure of the system is gradually changed. To cite a specific example, Fischer and Rahlfs suspended weighed samples of aluminum halides from a calibrated steel spring and, while maintaining constant temperature, allowed the pressure on the samples to change slowly. The equilibrium pressures were signalled by marked increases in dW/dP, the rate of change of mass with pressure. These particular experiments were much more easily performed than those in which the pressures were maintained at constant levels while the temperatures were changed.

The foregoing methods require that the system be in equilibrium. Other equilibrium methods have also been devised. A number of methods which depend upon a nonequilibrium state have also been used in molten salt systems. These include the Knudsen effusion method, molecular beams, mass spectrometry, and transpiration measurements. Let us examine the last in some detail.

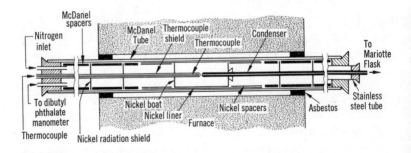

Figure 7–1 Apparatus for measurement of vapor pressure by transpiration method. (From Sense, Alexander, Bowman, and Filbert, ref. 5.)

The transpiration, or flow method, is one of the simpler techniques for the measurement of vapor pressures. A sketch of a typical apparatus designed by Sense and co-workers (1957) is shown in Figure 7–1. A known volume of inert carrier gas at constant pressure is passed over the heated sample at a slow, but constant rate, so that saturation is obtained. The salt vapor carried by the gas is collected and weighed. This information makes it possible to calculate the equilibrium vapor pressure directly from the known amount of carrier gas and the total pressure, assuming an ideal gas mixture. This type of experiment requires some knowledge of the nature of the gaseous species formed by the salt. Careful attention must be given to a number of experimental details such as flow rate of the carrier gas, correction for diffusion, and segregation effects. The interested reader should refer to the original literature for additional details.

(4) Electrical Conductivity

The measurement of electrical conductivity in fused salts utilizes techniques which are essentially the same as those used in aqueous systems. The important differences are the following:

(1) measurements in fused salts are made at much higher temperatures

(2) molten ionic salts are much better conductors than water so that the cell constants are of a different order of magnitude than those used in aqueous systems

(3) materials of construction which are adequate for measurements in aqueous systems are not useful for fused salts, primarily because of chemical attack at high temperature.

(5) Analytical Methods

In order to understand the nature of chemical reactions in fused salts it is essential that some means of analyzing the reaction products be devised. Spectroscopic methods including visible, ultraviolet, infrared, Raman, n.m.r., X-ray and neutron diffraction have all been used. Determinations may be made while the salts are still fluid, or after they have been allowed to solidify. Because of the high temperatures involved, the performance of experiments in the liquid state have required special modifications of conventional instruments.

83

One example is the modification of the sample compartment of the Cary Model 14 spectrophotometer as described by Young and White. A sketch of their design is shown in Figure 7–2. Appropriate modifications for measuring absorption spectra of molten salts have been designed for the Beckman DU spectrophotometer by Sundheim and Greenberg, for the Perkin-Elmer Model 21 spectrophotometer by Greenberg and Hallgren, while Bues has described the measurement of Raman Spectra in molten salts. Measurements of n.m.r. and e.s.r. spectra have been relatively few, but some have been reported by Roland and Bromberg and Brown. The most complete report involving X-ray and neutron diffraction studies on molten salt systems is that of Levy, et al.

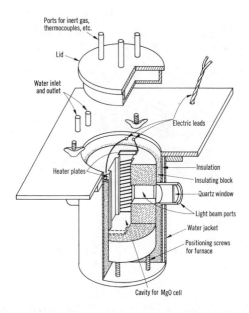

Figure 7–2 High-temperature cell assembly designed for use with Cary Model 14-M spectrophotometer. [Young and White, *Anal. Chem.*, **31**, 1892 (1959).]

7–C SOME APPLICATIONS OF FUSED SALT CHEMISTRY

One of the more important of the commercial applications of fused salt technology is the electrolysis of molten alkali metal halides. This process is basic for the commercial preparation of most of the highly reactive alkali metals. These elements are too electropositive to be prepared conveniently either by conventional chemical reduction methods or by the electrolytic reduction of aqueous solutions of their salts. In terms of sheer dollar volume, however, the electrolytic reduction of alumina, i.e., anhydrous aluminum oxide, in molten cryolite, Na_3AlF_6, stands out. Since these applications have been known for many years and are well described in many texts, we shall be concerned with a few examples of current research which may further extend the utilization of fused salt technology.

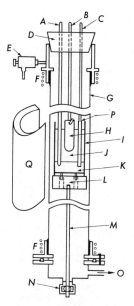

Figure 7–3 Apparatus used by Johnson, ref. 14, for preparation of pure thorium from molten halide mixture. *A*, alumina thermocouple well; *B*, tantalum anode hanger; *C*, tantalum cathode lead; *D*, rubber stopper; *E*, argon outlet valve; *F*, water-cooled flanges with Apiezon W seal; *G*, Vycor furnace tube; *H*, thorium anode; *I*, Pyrex beaker; *J*, fused salt; *K*, molten zinc cathode; *L*, steel platform; *M*, steel stirrer; *N-O*, ring seal for stirrer; *P*, ceramic insulator on cathode lead; *Q*, clam shell furnace around Vycor tube.

The nuclear industry, with its unusual metallurgical needs, has created a requirement for the reprocessing and re-enrichment and purification of the cores or blankets of breeder type reactors. As an illustration of a process which utilizes fused salt techniques, let us study an experiment by R. E. Johnson (ref. 14) which describes the preparation of pure metallic thorium by the anodic dissolution of impure thorium.

The apparatus used by Johnson is shown in Figure 7–3. The electrolytic process was carried out under an argon atmosphere in a fused salt medium composed of 150 g. of LiCl, 150 g. of KCl, and containing varying amounts of $ThCl_4$. The cathode was of molten zinc which, being more dense than the molten salt, separated as a liquid phase beneath the melt. An anode of impure thorium (the material being purified) was suspended in the molten salt mixture. The electrical leads, both that to the impure thorium anode and those which ran through the melt to the molten zinc cathode, were made of solid tantalum metal. Electrolysis was carried out at 600°C. The cathode current efficiency was measured as a function of the $ThCl_4$ concentration, thorium concentration in the zinc, and current density. Conditions were established which made possible the deposition of thorium metal from fused $LiCl$-KCl-$ThCl_4$ melts at essentially 100% efficiency. A maximum practical thorium concentration in the zinc of about 15% was achieved.

7–D   ACID-BASE THEORY IN MOLTEN NITRATES

Some interesting analogies which exist between water and fused alkali metal nitrates have been studied by Duke and co-workers. For example, the parallelism in the acid-base dissociation

$$NO_3^- \rightleftarrows NO_2^+ + O^{-2}$$
$$H_2O \rightleftarrows H^+ + OH^-$$

has been pointed out. The degree of dissociation of the nitrate ion is considerably less than that of water, but the nitryl ion, NO_2^+, is a stronger acid than is the proton and the oxide ion a stronger base than hydroxide. The addition of a strong acid, A, to a molten nitrate should give rise to a considerable concentration of nitryl ion as a consequence of the reaction

$$O^{-2} + A \rightleftarrows AO^{-2}$$

which would shift the nitrate ion dissociation equilibrium to the right. The addition of a base stronger than the oxide ion should increase the concentration of this ion. Such a base has not yet been discovered. However, two acids have been found to react with fused nitrates to form the nitryl ion, NO_2^+.

The acids, dichromate and pyrosulfate ions, react in the following manner:

$$Cr_2O_7^{-2} + NO_3^- \rightleftarrows NO_2^+ + 2\,CrO_4^{-2}$$
$$S_2O_7^{-2} + NO_3^- \rightleftarrows NO_2^+ + 2\,SO_4^{-2}$$

There exists no direct experimental method by which the nitryl ion concentration can be measured. The preparation of an electrode based on the reaction

$$NO_2 \rightleftarrows NO_2^+ + e^-$$

which would involve bubbling nitrogen dioxide over platinum has been suggested but not yet studied. Instead, the amount of NO_2^+ has been measured using a method based upon its rate of reaction with nitrate

$$NO_2^+ + NO_3^- \rightleftarrows 2\,NO_2 + 1/2\,O_2$$

The rate of formation of NO_2 is proportional to the NO_2^+ concentration. In a solution of dichromate in a molten nitrate the rate of formation of NO_2 gas is given by

$$\frac{d[NO_2]}{dt} = -\frac{d[A]}{dt} = k[NO_2^+]$$

The term $[A]$ is the total acid concentration and is equal to the sum of the dichromate and nitryl ion concentrations. There would be no change in $[A]$ if NO_2^+ did not decompose irreversibly into insoluble NO_2 and O_2. In the reaction with dichromate which produces the NO_2^+, the equilibrium lies so far to the left that $[NO_2^+]$ is negligible compared with $[Cr_2O_7^{-2}]$. This makes $[A] = [Cr_2O_7^{-2}]$, and after writing the expression for the equilibrium quotient, the following rate expression was derived

$$\frac{-d[Cr_2O_7^{-2}]}{dt} = \frac{kK[Cr_2O_7^{-2}]}{[CrO_4^{-2}]^2}$$

In this equation K is the equilibrium constant for the reaction. Although this rate equation was found to be quite accurate, k and K are not separable and $[NO_2^+]$ could not be calculated.

However, pyrosulfate is a much stronger acid than dichromate and the equilibrium reaction, $S_2O_7^{-2} + NO_3^- \rightleftarrows NO_2^+ + 2\,SO_4^{-2}$, was found to proceed sufficiently to the right so that $[NO_2^+]$ was no longer negligible. Now

$$[A] = [S_2O_7^{-2}] + [NO_2^+]$$

and

$$[NO_2^+] = \frac{K[A]}{K + [SO_4^{-2}]^2}$$

Since

$$K = \frac{[NO_2^+][SO_4^{-2}]^2}{[S_2O_7^{-2}]}$$

and $[S_2O_7^{-2}]$ may be replaced by $[A] - [NO_2^+]$ in the equilibrium expression, the rate expression becomes

$$\frac{-d[A]}{dt} = \frac{kK}{K + [SO_4^{-2}]^2}\,[A]$$

Experimentally, $[SO_4^{-2}]$ is much larger than $[A]$ and the bracketed portion of the rate expression is constant for a given sulfate ion concentration. $[A]$ was determined by removing samples from the melt at various times, dissolving them in water, and titrating the acid produced.

If k′ is defined as

$$k' = \frac{kK}{K + [SO_4^{-2}]^2}$$

a series of k′ values at different sulfate concentrations could be determined. Rearrangement of the preceding equation in reciprocal form gives

$$\frac{1}{k'} = \frac{1}{k} + \frac{[SO_4^{-2}]^2}{kK}$$

A plot of $1/k'$ *vs.* $[SO_4^{-2}]^2$ should give a straight line intercepting the ordinate at $1/k$, and the abscissa at $-K$. In this manner, the data shown in Table 7–2 were obtained.

Table 7–2

Data on Rate and Equilibrium Constants for the Reaction of Pyrosulfate with Fused Nitrate

$k(min.^{-1})$	T°C	$K_{S_2O_7^{-2}}$
0.038	235	0.026
0.096	275	0.038

7–E SPECTROPHOTOMETRIC STUDIES IN MOLTEN FLUORIDE SALTS

The subject of electronic absorption spectroscopy of transition metal ions in fused salts is ably discussed in recent reviews by Smith and Gruen. To accomplish the more limited scope of the immediate presentation, let us examine some recent papers by Young and White which are concerned with absorption spectra in molten fluorides.

The cell assembly designed by these investigators was intended specifically for use with a Cary Model 14-M Spectrophotometer and is shown in Figure 7–2. One of the more difficult problems which required solution was the highly corrosive nature of the molten fluoride melts toward materials used to construct the absorption cells. Several types of sample holders were devised using different materials of construction. The cell finally chosen was one bearing highly polished windows made of crystalline magnesium oxide. The transmission of this material is satisfactory over the range from 300 to 1800 mμ. Although magnesium oxide is quite inert toward molten alkali fluorides, it is only moderately inert to alkali fluoride mixtures containing dissolved transition metal ions and it is corroded by uranium and zirconium fluorides. The solution of the latter problem was critical because of the importance of determining uranium concentrations in these solutions. This difficulty was overcome by the use of the "pendent drop method." Instead of having the sample of molten material confined by the walls of the cell, a molten drop was suspended in the light beam and in this manner the problem of contact with cell walls was eliminated. The drop was suspended in a platinum wire ring, in a wound platinum coil, or in a cylindrical platinum tube having open ends.

The molten drop naturally assumes a lens shape and this presented optical difficulties. This problem was solved, to a large degree, by making the drop large relative to the area of the focal plane of the light beam and by allowing only the light which actually passed through the sample to impinge upon the detector. This made it necessary to mask out 90–95% of the reference beam in order to achieve double-beam balance. In spite of these difficulties, satisfactory absorption spectra were obtained.

Actual sample preparation involved the heating, under dry argon, of weighed amounts of solvent and solute in platinum crucibles at temperatures from 600–650°C until a clear melt was formed. The solutions were quenched to room temperature under a dry argon atmosphere and the solid samples were removed from the crucible in a dry-box. Afterwards the sample was powdered and placed either in the MgO cell or in a platinum cup. These were then heated under a dry argon atmosphere, transferred to the cell assembly and heated to the molten state.

When the pendent drop technique was used, the platinum tube sample holder was lowered into the platinum cup containing the molten sample and then raised into the light beam. This was done by means of a movable cylindrical ceramic holder into which the tube was mounted. Two of the spectra recorded by these investigators are shown in Figure 7–4.

7–F   SPECTRA OF THE TRANSITION METAL IONS OF THE FIRST SERIES

These ions are characterized by the filling in of the $3d$ energy level which leads to their most characteristic properties, viz., paramagnetism, variable oxidation states, and color. The last property is a result of electronic transitions which occur within the $3d$ energy levels. In order to compare the spectra of the common transition metal ions as they are observed in molten salts with those in water solution, it is necessary to review very briefly the implications of crystal field theory.

In an isolated, gaseous transition metal ion, the d orbitals possess five-fold degeneracy, i.e., they are equal in energy. Thus, the spectroscopic ground term for an isolated Co(III) ion which possesses a $3d^6$ outer electron configuration, in accordance with Hund's rules

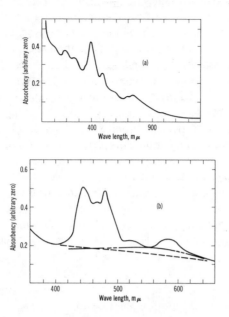

Figure 7–4 Spectrum of (a)-samarium fluoride in molten lithium fluoride: temp., 860°C, path length, 0.87 cm, Sm conc. 4.0% (w/w); (b)-praseodymium fluoride in the same solvent: temp., 896°C, path length, 0.94 cm, Pr conc. 2.5% (w/w). [Young and White, *Anal. Chem.*, **32**, 1658 (1960)].

of maximum multiplicity, is ^5D. The six electrons are distributed among the five degenerate d orbitals, with two electron spins paired. This may be illustrated in the following manner

$$Co^{+3} \quad ⇅ \quad ↑ \quad ↑ \quad ↑ \quad ↑$$

The arrows represent the electrons and their directions indicate the spins. When the Co(III) ion is dissolved in water, however, it is no longer free, but finds itself in a field of six nearest (coordinated) water dipoles arranged about it in a regular octahedral configuration, i.e.,

OH₂
H₂O———|———OH₂
Co⁺³
H₂O———————OH₂
OH₂

91

If, instead of water molecules, any other ligand, such as NH_3 or an ion such as Cl^-, Br^-, etc., is oriented about the central metal atom, there results some interaction between negatively charged electrons in the outermost d orbitals of the metal ion and the coordinated anions or the negative ends of the ligand dipoles. The result of this interaction is that the d orbitals, degenerate in the free ion, under the influence of the crystal field or ligand field lose this degeneracy and split into new levels of varying energy and degeneracy. The degree and type of splitting depend upon the geometric symmetry of the field. In a regular octahedral environment the five-fold degenerate d levels are split into a three-fold degenerate level of lower energy known as the t_{2g} orbitals and a two-fold degenerate level of higher energy known as the e_g orbitals. In a tetrahedral environment, the order is inverted, i.e., the e_g orbitals are of lower energy. The t_{2g} levels are comprised of the d_{xy}, d_{yz} and d_{xz} orbitals, while the $d_{x^2-y^2}$ and d_{z^2} orbitals make up the e_g levels. An energy level diagram for the d orbital splittings is shown in Figure 7–5.

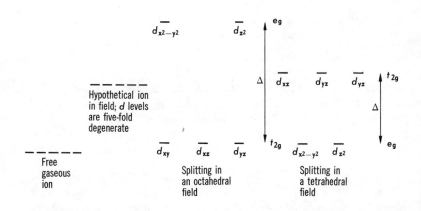

Figure 7–5 Splitting of the d energy levels in an octahedral field and in a tetrahedral field.

The symbol, Δ, represents the total splitting between the t_{2g} and e_g orbitals. The terms $10D_q$ or $E_2 - E_1$ have also been used to represent the quantity.

92

If there are one, two or three electrons in an octahedral complex ion, they can enter the three t_{2g} levels with parallel spins. In the case of Co(III) complexes, in the vast majority of cases, the six available electrons enter the lower t_{2g} level and all are paired. This means that the ligand, or crystal field energy is greater than the exchange energy (energy gained when the maximum spin multiplicity is maintained).

$$ ⑪ \quad ⑪ \quad ⑪ $$

In the case of the Ti(III) ion, with its single d electron, the ground state is $(t_{2g})^1(e_g)^0$, a ^2D state. When the single d electron absorbs energy, it enters the excited state which is $(t_{2g})^0(e_g)^1$ and what we observe is a $t_{2g} \rightarrow e_g$ transition. The energy level diagram for a d^1 ion is shown in Figure 7–6. The case of a d^9 configuration is very similar to that for the d^1; the transition observed is that from the ground state, $(t_{2g})^6(e_g)^3 \rightarrow (t_{2g})^5(e_g)^4$. As the ligand field strength is increased the observed absorption corresponding to this transition occurs at successively higher frequencies.

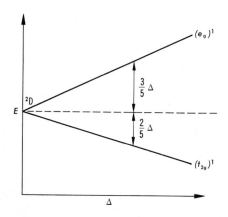

Figure 7–6 Energy level diagram for a d^1 ion. (Orgel, *An Introduction to Transition Metal Chemistry*, Methuen, 1960.)

When the situation is one in which we are dealing with more than one, but less than nine d electrons, the energy level diagrams become very complicated. The interpretation of observed spectra in terms of such diagrams is well beyond the scope of the present coverage.

Crystal-field transitions in molten chloride melts have generally been observed to occur at frequencies lower than those observed for the corresponding transitions in aqueous solution or in hydrated crystals. The $^4A_{2g} \rightarrow {}^4T_{2g}$ transition of Cr(III) which occurs at 17,600 cm^{-1} in aqueous solution has been observed at 12,500 cm^{-1} in a eutectic of LiCl and KCl at 400°. This suggests that Δ due to an octahedron of chloride ions is about 75% of that arising from an octahedron of water dipoles.

In most cases, the spectra of molten salt solutions either closely resemble the spectra of complexes of known cubic configuration or they behave in the manner predicted by crystal-field theory for cubic splitting. However, a number of cases have been noted in which the spectra in molten salt solutions deviate in a number of ways from the behavior predicted for a simple cubic configuration. These deviations have been interpreted in terms of distortions of the simple cubic symmetry.

When the coordination number is lowered from six to four, there is a lowering in the energy of the transition. This reflects a decrease in the value of Δ for tetrahedral as opposed to octahedral coordination. In chloride melts one example of the departure from cubic symmetry exhibited by $3d$ ion spectra is in the fine structure of the bands. Often, they show shoulders and subsidiary maxima. In other cases, the intensity of the absorptions are much higher than expected when compared with the spectra of the same ions in an octahedral symmetry. Generally, the absorption bands for tetrahedral complexes are of considerably greater intensity than those for octahedral complexes.

Let us examine the data of Gruen and McBeth (1963), who measured the spectrum of Ti(III) in LiCl-KCl eutectic at temperatures from 400–1000°, as well as in CsGaCl$_4$ at temperatures from 600–900°. The band positions were found to undergo a great deal of change when either the chloride ion activity or the temperature was changed. In LiCl-KCl eutectic, at 400°, Ti(III) exhibited a broad absorption band in the 8000–15,000 cm^{-1} region which was further characterized by a shoulder at 10,000 cm^{-1} and a maximum at 13,000 cm^{-1}. With increasing temperature a new band was observed to develop with a maximum at 7000 cm^{-1}, the intensity of which increased markedly as the temperature was raised. When the solvent was made up of an equimolar mixture of CsCl and GaCl$_3$ at 900° a band maximum was found near 8000 cm^{-1}, with shoulders at both higher and lower frequencies.

94

The observed spectral behavior was interpreted in terms of an equilibrium between octahedral and tetrahedral species

$$TiCl_6{}^{-3} \rightleftarrows TiCl_4{}^- + 2\,Cl^-$$

It has been predicted that a change in the coordination number from six to four should be accompanied by a decrease in the frequency of the transition and an increase in the intensity of the absorption band. Experimental observations were consistent with these predictions. At 400° in LiCl-KCl, in which $TiCl_6{}^{-3}$ should predominate, two maxima were observed at 10,000 and 13,000 cm^{-1} with molar absorptivities of ~5 and an oscillator strength of 1×10^{-4}. In molten CsGaCl$_4$ at 900° in which $TiCl_4{}^-$ should predominate, an absorption band at 8000 cm^{-1} was observed with a molar absorptivity of ~50 and an oscillator strength of ~1.5×10^{-3}.

On the basis of purely chemical considerations, the conclusions are perfectly self-consistent. Because of the stability of $GaCl_4{}^-$, the activity of Cl$^-$ in CsGaCl$_4$ melts is lower than in the LiCl-KCl eutectic and the equilibrium for the Ti(III) halide species is shifted to the right, in the direction of lower coordination.

7–G SOLUTIONS OF METALS WITH MOLTEN SALTS

Since the alkali metals are manufactured by electrolysis of their molten salts, the subject of solutions of metals in their molten salts has a history which is older than most chemists suspect. However, the significant developments in this field have occurred during the last two decades. Recent reviews by Bredig and Corbett discuss these developments in a thorough and capable manner.

The most significant and best understood investigations have dealt with solutions of metals in their own molten halides. Salts which bear oxygen-containing anions have not been widely studied since they decompose by reaction with the dissolved metal. Although precise knowledge about metal-metal halide systems is quite limited, several important conclusions appear to be well established.

Bredig has pointed out the convenience of dividing solutions of metals in their molten halides into two principal groups:

A. The first group is one in which the solutions acquire the metallic character of the solute. These are true solutions of the metals and represent a unique metallic state. Although they possess some similarities to solutions of the alkali metals in liquid ammonia, there is a fundamental difference which is due primarily to the high dielectric of the molten salt solvent and the fact that the latter contains cations of the metal which is dissolved. A majority of the solutions in this category are actually in the semi-conductor class since the electronic carriers have a negative temperature coefficient of electrical resistance.

B. The second group is characterized by those solutions in which a chemical reaction occurs between the metal solute and its molten salt. The metal assumes a valence state lower than that encountered in its ordinary salts. This class is often designated as "subhalide solutions."

It is to be remembered that differences between the two classes are not clearly defined. Basically, one distinguishes between electrons derived from the dissolved metal which in one case remain mobile and in the other become in some manner associated with the cations of the melt to produce a lower valence state.

The alkali metal-alkali halide systems are typical of group A. They exhibit relatively simple phase diagrams as shown in Figure 7–7 for the potassium metal-potassium halide systems. In all of these systems the melting point of the ionic alkali halide is very much higher than that of the metal, e.g., KCl, m.p. $1043°K$; K, m.p. $337°K$. This means that areas of interest in the phase diagrams are those in the vicinity of the melting points of the salts, and at higher temperatures. Although the solubility of the metal in the salts is appreciable at higher temperatures, it is exceedingly small in the eutectics. In the alkali metal-alkali halide systems, as metal is added to the salt, the melting point of the latter is lowered until the monotectic* point is reached. Just above the horizontal line passing through the monotectic point, e.g., at $849°$ for KF-K system, there is one region where one solid and one liquid phase coexist and another in which two liquids, one salt-rich (region A) and the other metal-rich (region B) coexist. The compositions of the two liquid phases approach each other with increasing temperature until they become equal at the critical solution temperature ($904°$), i.e., the maxima in the temperature-composition curves. At, and above this temperature, there exists a single liquid phase. Below the monotectic temperature a solution of the salt in liquid metal is in equilibrium with a very dilute solid solution of the metal in the salt.

---

* This is the point at which equilibrium exists between two liquids and one solid, the latter having a composition not intermediate between that of the two liquids.

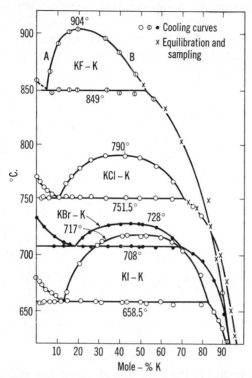

Figure 7–7 Temperature-composition phase diagrams for potassium metal-potassium halide systems. [Johnson and Bredig, *J. Phys. Chem.*, **62**, 606 (1958).]

The phase diagrams for lithium, sodium, and potassium metals, with each of their halides, fit the general description just given. The order of solubility of the salt in the molten metal is K > Na > Li. The cesium-cesium halides differ from the other alkali metal-metal halide systems in that the liquids are miscible in all proportions.

The rubidium systems are intermediate between the potassium and cesium systems. The monotectic point is absent in the bromide system and a narrow temperature range of partial miscibility of only about 20°C has been observed in the fluoride, chloride and iodide systems. While there appears to be a well defined trend toward increased miscibility of the metal with the salt with increasing size of the halide, i.e., the critical solution temperature increases in the order $Br^- < Cl^- < F^-$, the trend appears to be reversed or diminished for the iodide. Another interesting trend is the increase in the metal content of the solution formed at the critical solution temperature with increasing size of halide ion as shown in Table 7–3.

The data for lithium are not included in Table 7–3 because they are incomplete. Those for rubidium have been estimated from its phase diagrams and follow the same trend as those for sodium and potassium. Cesium-cesium halide systems, it will be recalled, show miscibility in all proportions in the molten state.

Table 7–3

Critical Temperatures and Critical Solution Compositions for Systems of Sodium and Potassium with their Halides

MX-M MX	Salt m.p., °K	Temp., °K	Critical Solution Composition mole-% Alkali Metal, M
NaF	1268	1453	28
NaCl	1073	1353	50
NaBr	1020	1299	52
NaI	933	1306	59
KF	1131	1177	20
KCl	1043	1063	39
KBr	1007	1001	44
KI	954	990	50

Activity coefficients of the salts in the molten solutions have also been measured and have been found to increase from unity with increasing metal concentration. The positive deviations of the salt component from Raoult's law which decrease in the order K-KBr > Rb-RbBr > Cs-CsI follow the same trend as the critical solution temperatures, i.e., the deviations increase with decreasing size of the metal atom.

Although the coloration of molten alkali halides by excess metal has been recognized for many years, studies on the spectra of these systems have been relatively few in number and nondefinitive.

Studies on the electrical properties of these solutions have been more complete. The importance of electrons as electrical carriers in these solutions has been amply demonstrated. With the exception of the Na-NaF systems, all sodium and potassium systems were investigated and in every case an increase of specific conductivity was observed with increasing concentration of the metal in the melt. The electron carriers were estimated to contribute as much as 99.5%

to the conductivity of a K-KI solution containing 42 mole-% potassium.

Bronstein and Bredig (1958) plotted the apparent equivalent conductance of sodium and potassium in their halides as a function of the metal concentration (Figure 7–8). The steady rise in the equivalent conductance in the potassium systems is evident in the illustration, while in the sodium systems the curves appear to approach a minimum after which there should be a rise. In the latter case, measurements at higher sodium concentrations were obviated because of the limited solubility of sodium.

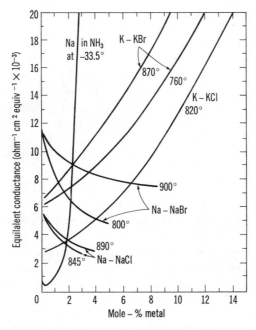

Figure 7–8 Equivalent conductances of solutions of alkali metals dissolved in their halides. (From Bronstein and Bredig, ref. 22.)

Electrons, in both solutions, must be able to function as carriers at infinite dilution of the metals. A most important consideration, in the sodium solutions, is the decrease in equivalent conductance which occurs with increasing sodium concentration. According to one view, the removal of electrons has been attributed to electron trapping through formation of Na_2 molecules. Such a view could be tested by measurements at higher temperatures. Under such conditions the diatomic sodium molecules should dissociate and a behavior like that of potassium should be observed. In the lithium systems, because of the relative stability of Li_2, electron trapping should occur to an even greater degree.

Another interesting aspect of the electrical conductivities of these systems is the large increase which is observed with increasing size of the halide ion. In the case of K in KX, for instance, the molar conductivities at infinite dilution increase in the following manner: K in KF, 800; in KCl, 2800; in KBr, 6000; in KI, 8100 ohm^{-1}cm^2 mole^{-1}. This trend has been attributed to the greater polarizability of the larger anions. The higher polarizabilities are believed to facilitate the electron transfer process. This conclusion is based largely upon analogies with electron transfer processes involving complex ions in solution.

The temperature dependence of the electrical conductivity is exceedingly important since it would distinguish between conduction of a metallic nature and that of the type encountered in semi-conductors. Unfortunately, such data have been very difficult to obtain. In solutions having very low metal concentrations, the temperature dependence has been found to be very slight. At higher metal concentrations, the temperature coefficient becomes negative. The latter behavior is typical of semi-conductors.

In summation, what has been found to be a convenient model, although not a specific one, is one in which, in the salt-rich region, electrons are substituted for anions, and, in the metal-rich phase, halide ions are substituted for electrons. In this view, the greater solubility of the salt in the metal, as one goes from lithium to cesium, can be related to the weaker forces which bind the larger atoms and the greater ease with which the halide ions, which are large, can be substituted for the larger metal atoms.

Pitzer (1962) has approached these systems from the viewpoint of an inter-mixing of electrons and anions and the application of the theory of regular solutions. The interested reader is referred to the original literature for familiarization with this treatment.

7–H METALS THAT DISSOLVE WITH SUBHALIDE FORMATION

Figure 7–9 shows the phase diagram for the $Hg\text{-}HgCl_2$ system according to Yosim and Mayer. Solid mercuric chloride remains stable up to 525°C. It then decomposes into a melt containing approximately 50 mole-% mercury and a small amount of the metal containing about seven mole-% of mercuric chloride in solution. From freezing point depression measurements and a knowledge of the heat of fusion, it was reasoned that the mercury was dissolved either as mercury atoms or as the subhalide, i.e.,

$$Hg + HgCl_2 \rightarrow Hg_2Cl_2$$

with Hg_2Cl_2 being the more probable species. Measurements of the electrical conductivity of these solutions suggest that Hg_2Cl_2 is not ionized in $HgCl_2$. An interesting physical property of these solutions is the increase in the intensity of their color with increase in temperature or in mercury concentration.

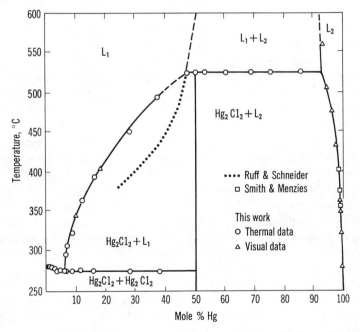

Figure 7–9 The mercury-mercuric chloride system. (From Yosim and Mayer, ref. 24.)

The existence and stability of Hg_2Cl_2 is well recognized from studies of the aqueous chemistry of mercury and its compounds, but the formation of Cd_2^{+2} compounds is still not unequivocally established in spite of the fact that Cd-CdCl₂ melts have been widely studied.

It was known as early as 1910 that the dissolution of cadmium metal in cadmium chloride lowered the conductivity of the latter. The diamagnetism of the melt suggested that the dissolved metal is not present as Cd^+, which is paramagnetic, but as Cd_2^{+2} or Cd^0. Data on the heat of fusion were interpreted as being in better agreement with the assumption of Cd_2^{+2} rather than Cd^0 as the solute species, but thermodynamic values used in support of these conclusions were soon questioned because of a subsequent large change in the value determined for the heat of fusion of $CdCl_2$ itself. The picture has been further confused by a lack of adequate reproducibility in the published phase diagrams.

The electrical conductivity data, first reported by Aten (1910) have been found to be reproducible with modern techniques. One reasonably sound conclusion, based on electrical conductivity experiments, is that the depression in the specific conductance which is observed upon addition of the metal results largely from a decrease in the self-diffusion coefficients (D) of cadmium and chloride ions. One choice of solute species was Cd_2^{+2} and Cd_2Cl^+ and it was concluded that $D(Cd_2^{+2})$ or $D(Cd_2Cl^+)$ must be smaller than $D(Cd^{+2})$ or $D(CdCl^+)$. Together with measurements of the moving boundary, it was inferred that the migrating species are principally $CdCl^+$ and Cd_2^{+2}. Although the existence of Cd_2X_2 is still largely based upon indirect evidence, the isolation of stable, diamagnetic $Cd_2(AlCl_4)_2$ by Corbett, Burkhard and Druding (1961) offers clear-cut evidence for the existence of cadmium in the $+1$ oxidation state.

Corbett (ref. 1, Ch. VI) has discussed the lanthanide metal-lanthanide halide systems. Studies of the temperature-composition phase diagrams have led to a number of interesting observations. Among these is evidence for the existence of a $+2$ oxidation state for the first four inner transition elements. For example, the separation of the compounds $PrCl_{2.3}$, $PrBr_{2.38}$ and $NdCl_2$ has been reported. The presence of $PrCl_2$ in Pr-$PrCl_3$ melts has been supported by vapor pressure studies by Novikov and Polyachenok. Other examples of divalent lanthanides, evidence for whose existence is based upon the nature of the metal-metal halide systems, are LaI_2, PrI_2 and NdI_2.

In order to interpret the behavior of lanthanide metal-lanthanide halide systems with respect to their electrical conductivities, the presence of a solute, the stability of which increases in going from lanthanum to neodymium, has been assumed. The divalent metal ion appears to be the most probable of such species.

7–I CONCLUDING REMARKS

It has been possible to cover only a few of the many interesting aspects of fused salt chemistry in this book, and then not in any detailed manner. The challenge of experimentation with molten salt systems is being met by the chemist as measurements are being made at higher and higher temperatures. The theories of liquids and solutions are finding interesting testing grounds among fused-salt systems.

Even a brief review of the Table of Contents of the collected essays of Sundheim and Blander will reveal that studies in molten salt systems have been overwhelmingly concerned with measurements of the physical properties of these systems and the theoretical interpretations of these measurements. There is a glaring lack of information on fused salt systems as media for chemical reactions. The potential here appears to be great, indeed. The existence of certain oxidation states in fused salts, e.g., Cd(I), unknown in aqueous systems or other "conventional" nonaqueous solvents, has been demonstrated. What about the behavior of organic compounds in these solvents at high temperatures? This question certainly invites a great deal of investigation.

Exercises

1. Suggest a preparative reaction, either organic or inorganic, which you think can be successfully carried out in a molten salt. Give details concerning the procedures you would use to set up the experiment and the methods you would require to isolate and identify the products of the reaction.
2. Following are listed a few topics suitable for oral or written reports. You may, of course, find others which may be of greater interest to you.

   a. Vibrational spectra in fused salts
   b. Electrical conductivity in fused salts
   c. Alkali halide vapors
   d. Titrations in molten salt media
   e. Thermodynamic properties of molten salt systems
   f. The structure of ionic liquids
   g. Complex ions in molten halides

References

1. *Fused Salts*, B. R. Sundheim, Ed., McGraw-Hill, 1964.
2. J. D. Corbett and F. R. Duke, *Technique of Inorganic Chemistry*, H. B. Jonassen and A. Weissberger, Eds., Vol. I, Ch. 3, Interscience, 1963.
3. O. Ruff and B. Bergdahl, *Z. anorg. allgem. Chem.*, **106**, 76 (1919).
4. W. Fischer, O. Rahlfs, and B. Benze, *ibid.*, **205**, 1 (1932).
5. K. A. Sense, C. A. Alexander, R. E. Bowman, and R. B. Filbert, Jr., *J. Phys. Chem.*, **61**, 337 (1957).
6. S. N. Flengas and T. R. Ingraham, *Can. J. Chem.*, **35**, 1139 (1957).
7. J. P. Young and J. C. White, *Anal. Chem.*, **31**, 1892 (1959).
8. B. R. Sundheim and J. Greenberg, *Rev. Sci. Instr.*, **27**, 703 (1956).
9. J. Greenberg and L. J. Hallgren, *J. Chem. Phys.*, **35**, 180 (1961).
10. W. Bues, *Physicochemical Measurements at High Temperatures*, Ch. 12, J. O'M. Bockris, J. L. White and J. D. MacKenzie, Eds., Butterworths, 1959.
11. T. J. Rowland and J. P. Bromberg, *J. Chem. Phys.*, **29**, 626 (1958).
12. J. Brown, *Lawrence Radiation Laboratory Report*, UCRL-9944, Dec. 12, 1961.
13. H. A. Levy, P. A. Agron, M. A. Bredig, and M. D. Danford, *Ann. N.Y. Acad. Sci.*, **79**, 762 (1960).
14. R. E. Johnson, *J. Electrochem. Soc.*, **109**, 989 (1962).
15. F. R. Duke and M. L. Iverson, *J. Am. Chem. Soc.*, **80**, 5061 (1958).
16. F. R. Duke and S. Yamamoto, *ibid.*, **81**, 6378 (1959).
17. F. R. Duke, *J. Chem. Ed.*, **39**, 57 (1962).
18. G. P. Smith, p. 427 in *Molten Salt Chemistry*, M. Blander, Ed., Interscience, 1964; D. M. Gruen, Ch. 5 in ref. 1.
19. J. P. Young and J. C. White, *Anal. Chem.* **32**, 1658 (1960).
20. D. M. Gruen and R. L. McBeth, *Pure Appl. Chem.*, **6**, 23 (1963).
21. M. A. Bredig, p. 367 in *Molten Salt Chemistry*, M. Blander, Ed., Interscience, 1964; J. D. Corbett, Ch. 6 in ref. 1.
22. H. R. Bronstein and M. A. Bredig, *J. Am. Chem. Soc.*, **80**, 2077 (1958).
23. K. S. Pitzer, *J. Am. Chem. Soc.*, **84**, 2025 (1962).
24. S. J. Yosim and S. W. Mayer, *J. Phys. Chem.*, **64**, 909 (1960).
25. A. H. W. Aten, *Z. physik. Chem.*, **73**, 578 (1910).
26. J. D. Corbett, W. J. Burkhard and L. F. Druding, *J. Am. Chem. Soc.*, **83**, 76 (1961).
27. G. I. Novikov and O. G. Polyachenok, *Zh. Neorgan. Khim.*, **7**, 1209 (1962).
28. H. Bloom, "Molten Electrolytes," Ch. 3 in Vol. 2 of *Modern Aspects of Electrochemistry*, J. O'M. Bockris, Ed., Butterworths, 1964.

INDEX

Acids and bases
  Arrhenius theory, 9
  Brönsted-Lowry theory, 10
  ionotropy, 12, 57
  Lewis theory, 14
  in liquid SO_2, 49
  in molten nitrates, 86
  solvent systems concept, 12, 57
  theories of, 9
Alkali metals
  extraction of, by phenols, 71
  solutions of, in fused salts, 96
  solutions of, in liquid ammonia, 22
Ammonia
  hydrogen isotope exchange in, 32
  organic reactions in, 28
  physical properties of, 22
  reactions in, 26
  solubility of metals in, 22
Ammonolysis, 28
Amphoterism
  in liquid ammonia, 27

BAMBP, 4-*sec*-butyl-2-
  (α-methylbenzyl) phenol, 71
Bifluoride ion, 38, 40
4-*sec*-Butyl-2-(α-methylbenzyl) phenol
  extraction of alkali metals by, 71

Carbonyl chloride
  (see Phosgene)
Cesium
  extraction of, by phenols, 71
Classification of solvents, 4
Complex compounds
  formation of, in liquid SO_2, 51
Coordination
  model, 16
  number, 2
Crystal field theory, 90

Dielectric constant(s), 5
  table of values, 6
Di-(2-ethylhexyl)phosphoric acid
  extraction of U(VI) by, 67
Diluent
  in solvent extraction, 61
Dipole moment, 5
Distribution ratio, 62

Electrolysis
  in fused salts, 85
  in liquid HF, 41
Ether
  extraction of metals by, 63
Extraction coefficient, 62

Ferric chloride
  extraction of, 63
Freons
  preparation of, in HF, 43
Fused salts
  electrolysis in, 85
  experimental methods in, 80
  melting points of, 80, 98
  solutions of metals in, 95
  spectra in, 89

Halometallic acids
  extraction of, 63
HDEHP, Di-(2-ethylhexyl)phosphoric
  acid, 60, 67
Hydration, 2
  of ions, 2, 3
  number, 2
Hydrocarbons
  acid-base behavior of, 32
Hydrogen bonding
  in ammonia, 36
  in hydrogen fluoride, 36
  in water, 5, 36
Hydrogen fluoride, 36
  acid-base reactions in, 39
  addition of, to unsaturated bonds, 44
  electrolysis in, 41
  organic reactions in, 41
  solubilities in, 37
Hydrolysis, 27

Ion-dipole, 5
Ionization
  of ammonia, 26
  of hydrogen fluoride, 40
  of organic compounds in liquid HF,
    39
  of sulfur dioxide, 49
  of water, 3
Ionotropy, 12, 57

Iron, extraction of
  (see Halometallic acids)
Isotope labelled compounds
  preparation in liquid ammonia, 34

Ligand field theory, see Crystal field
  theory

Measurements of physical properties
  in molten salts, 81
Metals
  solutions of, in fused salts, 95
  solutions of, in liquid ammonia, 22
Molten salts, see fused salts

Organic reactions
  in liquid HF, 41
  in liquid NH_3, 28
  in liquid SO_2, 56
Organophosphorus compounds
  in liquid-liquid extraction, 66

Partition-coefficient, 61
Petroleum refining
  use of SO_2 in, 55
Phosgene
  ionization of, 57
  radiotracer studies in, 57

Radioactive tracer studies
  in liquid SO_2, 52
  in phosgene, 57
Reagent
  in solvent extraction, 61

Solvates, 6
  with HF, 37
  with SO_2, 48
Solvation, 16
  by ammonia, 23
  by hydrogen fluoride, 38
  by water, 2

Solvent extraction, 59
  of alkali metals, 71
  of cesium, 71
  of halometallic acids, 63
  of uranium, 59, 67
Solvents
  acidic, 6
  amphoteric, 7
  aprotic, 7
  basic, 7
  classification of, 4
  differentiating, 7
  leveling, 7
  parent, 7
  protophylic, 6
Solvolytic reactions
  in liquid ammonia, 27
Spectrophotometry
  in fused salts, 89
Spectroscopic measurements
  in molten salts, 89, 90
Subhalides of metals, 100
Sulfur dioxide, 46
  acid-base reactions in, 49
  complex compound formation in, 51
  ionization of, 52
  organic reactions in, 56
  and petroleum refining, 55
  physical properties of, 47
  radiotracer studies in, 52
  solubilities in, 48

Thenoyltrifluoroacetone, TTA, 61
Transition metal ions
  spectra of, 89
Tri-n-butylphosphate, TBP, 60

Uranium
  extraction of, 59, 67

Water
  ionization of, 3
  limitations of, as a solvent, 2

1 2 3 4 5 6 7 8 9 0